The Water Vole

THE STORY OF ONE OF BRITAIN'S MOST ENDANGERED MAMMALS

CHRISTINE GREGORY
FOREWORD BY CHRIS PACKHAM

Published by Vertebrate Publishing, Sheffield.
www.v-publishing.co.uk

The
Water Vole

THE STORY OF ONE OF BRITAIN'S MOST
ENDANGERED MAMMALS

VP First published in 2016 by Vertebrate Publishing.

Vertebrate Publishing. Crescent House, 228 Psalter Lane, Sheffield S11 8UT.
www.v-publishing.co.uk

A CIP catalogue record for this book is available from the British Library.

ISBN: 978-1-910240-54-0

10 9 8 7 6 5 4 3 2 1

VP Designed and typeset in Adobe Garamond, The Sans and
Corda by Nathan Ryder. www.v-publishing.co.uk

Data maps of Derbyshire originally collated and designed by Debbie Alston and Dave Alston,
revised and re-coloured by Nathan Ryder.

Vertebrate Publishing is committed to printing on paper from sustainable sources.

FSC
www.fsc.org

MIX
Paper from
responsible sources
FSC® C106600

Printed and bound in Slovenia by Latitude Press Ltd.

For Tony

I WISH A WATER-RAT WOULD GLIDE
SLOWLY TO THE OTHER SIDE;
OR A DANCING SPIDER SIT
ON THE YELLOW FLAGS A BIT.

ON THE BRIDGE, KATE GREENAWAY (1885)

I'M TRULY SORRY MAN'S DOMINION
HAS BROKEN NATURE'S SOCIAL UNION,
AN' JUSTIFIES THAT ILL OPINION,
WHICH MAKES THEE STARTLE,
AT ME, THY POOR, EARTH-BORN COMPANION,
AN' FELLOW-MORTAL!

TO A MOUSE, ROBERT BURNS (1785)

OPPOSITE PAGE: Baby water vole in April, with forget-me-nots.

Contents

Adult water vole on a bed of water crowfoot in July.

Foreword

'Plop'. What would life be like without that characteristic 'plop', that little cork-pulling wet pop, which, if we are lucky, we can still hear as we wend along a wilder stream? It tells us that we have been spotted or heard by a nibbling water vole which has just leapt into the water, submerged and swum to safety. Luckier still and you might see a brief silvery flash as it paddles away downstream and then bobs up on to a mat of weed to continue chewing.

Round and brown, cricket ball-sized, with tiny ears and prominent, beady eyes, it looks cuddly and cute. But when you see its huge and sharp yellowy incisors, which can deal a decent bite, then you may want to reassess any anthropomorphism. Not that others haven't been tempted; Kenneth Grahame made the misnamed 'Ratty' a household name thanks to the water vole's role in *The Wind in the Willows*. No bad thing either because loving these creatures in any way possible may just be their salvation.

You see poor old 'Voley', and 'Mrs Voley' of course, are in big trouble. They have become the fastest declining mammal in the UK. Only the hedgehog is giving them a run for their money in the extinction race. And who would have thought it? They were once so common, but since canalisation of our waterways, pollution, abstraction and the unfortunate introduction of the American mink those 'plops' have become a sound of yesteryear. It's not all doom though as we understand the problems and have solutions in the form of habitat creation and reintroductions and in some places water voles are making a comeback.

This book provides pretty much all you need to know about these charming creatures: a field guide to the species, an encyclopaedia of volery and a volume of vole stuff to inform and interest all. Superb!

Chris Packham
2015

Adult water vole at a burrow entrance eating water crowfoot stems.

As he sat on the grass and looked across the river,
a dark hole in the bank opposite, just above the water's edge, caught his eye,
and dreamily he fell to considering what a nice snug dwelling-place it would make
for an animal with few wants and fond of a bijou riverside residence,
above flood level and remote from noise and dust.
As he gazed, something bright and small seemed to twinkle down in the heart of it,
vanished, then twinkled once more like a tiny star.
But it could hardly be a star in such an unlikely situation;
and it was too glittering and small for a glow-worm.
Then, as he looked, it winked at him, and so declared itself to be an eye:
and a small face began gradually to grow up around it, like a frame round a picture.

A brown little face with whiskers.

A grave round face, with the same twinkle in its eye that had first attracted his notice.

Small neat ears and thick silky hair.

It was the Water Rat!

THE WIND IN THE WILLOWS, KENNETH GRAHAME (1908)

Introduction

The water vole is Britain's fastest declining mammal. The Vincent Wildlife Trust conducted two national surveys, between 1989 and 1990, and 1996 and 1998, that first demonstrated the dramatic decline of this cherished species across Britain. Since then the number of sites once occupied by water voles has diminished even further, but they are doing well in many parts of Britain where conservation efforts have been focused. This book explores the fortunes past and present of the water vole, principally in Derbyshire, where just over a hundred years ago the great Victorian naturalist Jourdain described it as being 'found commonly in all our slow flowing streams'.

Over several years spent searching the rivers and canals of Derbyshire I have met many people who know and love their water voles; they can point to their burrows and places where they feed and they know when the voles have gone. I have also had numerous conversations about places where you 'can always see water voles', but when pressed I have found that 'always' is not this summer or even the last, and 'recently' may stretch back as far as five or even ten years. Today there is much talk of the 'new normal' where we have become used to scarcity and absence and any wildlife sighting is a cause for celebration and reassurance that all is well. In the spring and summer of 2014 I knew of several places where I was likely to see water voles; in 2015 I have struggled to find any at all.

Twenty-five years ago I moved to Youlgrave and lived with my family in a cottage perched high above Bradford Dale. Water voles were a common sight then, sitting close by the paths quietly munching their way through grasses or waterweeds they had dragged to their favoured haul-out platforms. Walks along the River Bradford were often punctuated with the distinctive plop sound of the water voles' watery vanishing trick. Around the mid 1990s the water voles vanished altogether and there were rumours of mink in the dale. In 2007, after a slow process of recolonising the river over previous years, the water voles were back and I spent many May mornings filming their antics on a camcorder amid the reeds at the southern end of the dale. On 25 June 2007, a summer deluge caused devastating floods and the deaths of two people in Sheffield. It also washed away this small colony of water voles. Four years later the river dried up completely and later flooded in 2012 in a pattern of extreme weather events experienced all over the country. Water voles have been seen sporadically on the Bradford since then but are currently scarce. Their fortunes on this little limestone river over the last quarter-century mirror a more general picture of a species under pressure from numerous threats.

Scientists are now in agreement that we face a biological crisis on Earth, so great that it is without precedent in the planet's history. In an article in *The Observer* on 21 June 2015, Jan Zalasiewicz, professor of palaeobiology at the University of Leicester, drew attention to new research indicating that the Earth is now on the brink of the 'sixth great mass extinction.'[1] The fifth was that which extinguished the dinosaurs. The current crisis is caused entirely by human activity. In a scientific paper published on 19 June 2015, Gerardo Ceballos of the National Autonomous University of Mexico and his colleagues judged that by the most conservative estimates the rate of vertebrate species extinctions since 1900 is between 10 and 100 times faster than long-term baseline rates (rates vary between different groups of animals with amphibians the fastest declining). The baseline or background rates are determined before 'the period during which *Homo sapiens* truly became a major force on the biosphere'. Since 1900, across all vertebrate groups, nine extinctions would be the baseline figure of naturally occurring extinctions. But in that time 468 species no longer exist, 69 of which are mammals. In his shocking article Zalasiewicz also draws attention to the sheer bulk of humanity as measured by scientist Vaclav Smil, of the University of Manitoba. Smil has calculated that humans now make up a third of land vertebrates in terms of mass and the animals that we keep to eat make up most of the other two thirds. All of the world's wild animals constitute just five per cent of land vertebrate biomass on earth. Humans have pushed wild animals to the brink. The water vole is close to extinction in Britain although it is not on the International Union for Conservation of Nature (IUCN) Red List of Threatened Species as it is still common elsewhere. But the story of the water vole's demise, long before the arrival of American mink, reflects the global picture of the replacement of wild animals with those kept to feed humans.

The immense wealth of scholarship and detailed research dedicated to the cause of the water vole leaves no room for doubt as to how we can best save it, but despite many public policy statements on protecting biodiversity, wildlife comes low on the government's agenda in austerity Britain. As Chris Packham says in the foreword to this book, love may just be the thing that saves the water vole – that and public pressure.

1) Zalasiewicz, 'The Earth stands on the brink of its sixth mass extinction and the fault is ours', *The Observer* (21 June 2015) [online] <http://www.theguardian.com/environment/2015/jun/21/mass-extinction-science-warning>

The first two parts of this book are focused on water voles, on what they are and how they live, with suggestions on how to find them. Part 3 summarises their legal status as a highly protected species. Part 4 provides a brief historical account of the water vole in Derbyshire, a guide to the principal rivers, their catchments and associated canals, and an outline of what is currently known of the water vole's presence across the county.

At the close of Part 4 there are sections outlining some of the principal threats to water vole survival in the remaining places where they can be found in Derbyshire. Part 5 has an account of the evolution of the water vole from fossil records of its earliest ancestors through to its accelerating decline. It explores some of the impacts that humans have had on this island from the first farmers through to the present day. There is also an account of water voles that do not live anywhere near water and which were once common and widespread in Britain. Changing land use is a constant theme in both parts 4 and 5, whereas Part 6 takes us to the most recent chapter in the decline of the water vole and the interlinked fortunes of three species of mammals, the otter, the mink and the water vole. The final part of the book looks to the future of the water vole with a consideration of the negative impacts of alien species, climate change and damaged ecosystems as well as the recovery of our rivers and the positive success stories of water vole reintroductions, habitat restoration and conservation.

I have had the privilege of meeting many inspiring people in the making of this book and seen many examples of the healing powers of nature. The sculpted slag heaps of north-east Derbyshire, where the hills once glowed red in the night from the volatile substances stacked high within them, are now cloaked with some of the finest and most extensive species-rich meadows in the county. Once raw, scarred, crumbling cliffs of eroded earth have been transformed into flower-decked banks on the River Derwent.

There is now an extremely high level of understanding of the optimum conditions needed for water voles to survive and even to thrive. There is much cause for hope here. Decades of dedicated research, analysis and an understanding of the causes of the decline and the precise requirements for the recovery of this species now aid recovery programmes. The effort and goodwill of thousands of volunteers who have put in many hours on species monitoring are aiding research and restoring habitats. The visionary work of conservationists has healed and restored some of the most blighted landscapes in Britain, and nature itself reclaims spaces and flourishes once the pressure is off. Many fishing clubs and estates who know the most about the complex web of life sustained by our rivers have seen beyond the private joys of fly fishing to the greater project of rebuilding the health of Derbyshire's glorious rivers and engaging local communities with their ideas.

We can all become part of the water vole's future. There is a list of organisations at the back of this book you can contact if you want to be involved in monitoring, reporting or habitat restoration work. The People's Trust for Endangered Species has launched a new national survey in which members of the public are invited to take part. So go out, start looking and get your children and grandchildren involved. Join your local Wildlife Trust and experience the joy of sharing the world with an animal common in Britain long before humans were part of the story.

Christine Gregory
October, 2015

'Avoiding a true sixth mass extinction will require rapid, greatly intensified efforts to conserve already threatened species and to alleviate pressures on their populations – notably habitat loss, over-exploitation for economic gain and climate change … but that window of opportunity is rapidly closing.'[2]

2) Ceballos, Ehrlich, Barnosky, Garcia, Pringle and Palmer, 'Accelerated modern human-induced species losses: Entering the sixth mass extinction' in *Science Advances*, Vol.1, No.5 (19 June 2015).

part 1

The Water Vole

What is a water vole?

Water rat, water ratten, water mole, craber, waterdog, earth hound, water campagnol.

The water vole *(Arvicola amphibius)* is a medium-sized rodent native to Britain.[1] It is in a group of animals called Cricetidae, which includes voles, lemmings and hamsters. The Cricetidae family is large but in Britain there are just four species, all of which are voles. Mainland Britain is home to the bank vole *(Myodes glareolus)*, the field vole *(Microtus agrestis)* and the water vole *(Arvicola amphibius)*. There is also an island population of voles that are similar to the field vole but considerably larger – the Orkney vole.

The water vole is by far the largest of the British voles and is similar in size to the common rat *(Rattus norvegicus)*. *Arvicola amphibius* is one of three types of water vole that inhabit the northern hemisphere across Europe, Asia, North Africa and parts of the Asian Peninsula. *Arvicola sapidus* occurs only in France and the Iberian Penisula, *Arvicola scherman* is present in France and Germany while our water vole, *Arvicola amphibius*, is widespread and can be found from Western Europe to eastern Siberia.[2]

The defining characteristics of the water vole are its large size relative to other voles, its rounded appearance, small ears, and a tail that is longer than that of other voles. It has open-rooted teeth that continue to grow throughout its life while being worn down by grinding on fibrous or hard plant material.

The water vole is widespread throughout mainland Britain and is present on both the Isle of Wight and Anglesey but it does not occur on most of the offshore islands or Ireland.

---

1) Linnaeus developed a system of naming and classifying species in the 18th century that we still use today (taxonomy). He named both *Mus terrestris* and *Mus amphibious* in 1758. *'Arvicola'* was first used to name the genus for all water voles in the 1790s. The scientific community has alternated between *'terrestris'* and *'amphibius'* or *'terrestris amphibius'* in recent years. Now *'amphibius'* is adopted as the correct name and will be used in this book. The historic names given are listed in Harris and Yalden, eds., *Mammals of the British Isles*, (2008).   2) Ibid.

Water vole eating an ash leaf; its lengthy tail (around two-thirds body length) is clearly visible.

IDENTIFYING THE WATER VOLE

There are really no other species similar to the water vole other than the common rat *(Rattus norvegicus)* although I have been put on the trail of a water vole by teenagers from London who had spotted a 'beaver' on the River Bradford near Youlgrave. On another occasion a family had seen a water vole with a very long nose by Linacre Reservoir near Chesterfield that turned out to be a (much smaller) water shrew.

A baby water vole could be mistaken for a bank vole or (the heavier) field vole, but the long tail, larger head and hind feet make identification clear.

Water vole pup, soon after its first forays out of the burrow, is similar in size to an adult field vole.

Adult bank vole, with smaller head and feet, short tail and more prominent ears than the baby water vole.

The water vole and the rat

Kenneth Grahame's misnaming of the water vole has added to confusion over its identity but his creation of the jaunty, raffish and kindly Ratty has done much to generate affection in Britain for the water vole. However the (understandable) confusion remains and has not helped the water vole's cause. It is unfortunate for the water vole that – viewed from a distance – it resembles the common rat, being of similar size and colour and often sharing the same waterside habitat. The rat is one of the most reviled and hated of animals while the water vole commands great affection. Yet the differences between these two large rodent species is often poorly understood. Those unfamiliar with the sight of a water vole are often confused by the length of the tail, believing that the tail should be short and stubby like that of some other voles. In recent years, population decline and decreased familiarity with the countryside have led to the water vole becoming a totally unknown species to many people – a large rodent that clearly isn't a mouse must be a rat. Mistaken identity has led to considerable persecution. I have heard numerous accounts of young lads taking pot shots at water voles with air guns.

The common rat is known to take both adult and young water voles. When common rats share the same territory as water voles, especially on urban watercourses, they can present a serious threat to the survival of a colony through predation, or fatalities caused by traps or poisoned bait that is put down to deal with rats. I have seen rats and water voles within a few metres of each other near ponds in both a town and country park. But while rats can be harmful to water voles, they have managed to coexist over many hundreds of years.

OPPOSITE PAGE: Common, or brown, rat (*Rattus norvegicus*).

THE WATER VOLE

The average length of the head and body of an adult male water vole is around 225 millimetres and its tail between half and two-thirds that length again. Females are slightly smaller with head and body measuring around 220 millimetres plus tail. Males' weight ranges between 246 and 386 grams and females' from 225 to 310 grams. Scottish water voles tend to be slightly smaller and lighter. The water vole has a rounded body and face with chubby cheeks and a blunt nose. Its ears are small, covered with fur, sit close to the head and are almost invisible. The eyes are small, dark, prominent and extremely beady in appearance. The water vole's top incisors have a brilliant orange enamel surface, which can be disconcerting when seen for the first time. These large incisors are used for digging as well as for biting into plant material. In common with other rodents, the water vole is equipped with 'fur brushes', which extend downward from the upper lip. When digging, the lips close off the gaps between the teeth to prevent soil being swallowed, while it pushes the soil out behind it using its hind feet.

The water vole's fur is a rich brown or chestnut colour across the back and sides with a paler brownish white underneath. The adult has long, gleaming guard hairs that give it a shaggy appearance, with an undercoat of finer hair that traps air and provides a degree of thermal insulation. Both adults and juveniles undergo two moults in the year, in the spring and in the autumn when their fur grows thicker and longer.

Young water voles are darker in appearance with denser, shorter and fluffier coats. Black or 'melanistic' populations of water voles have been recorded in various regions of Britain. In the north and north-west of Scotland most water voles are black, but some melanistic individuals have been seen elsewhere in Scotland and below the border. An account of the differences between Scottish, and English and Welsh water voles is given on page 137. While albino water voles are very rare there are often individuals in a colony that exhibit partial albinism in the form of small patches of white fur on the forehead, chest or tail tip.

The water vole's fur has no measure of protection against water, unlike the otter, and it can become waterlogged if it is immersed for too long. While water voles are competent swimmers, they have no specially adapted features such as webbed feet. They are able to stay under water for a maximum of 20 seconds.

The water vole's front feet or paws resemble hands, with four long 'fingers' with pointed claws with which it handles and manipulates its food. The hind feet have five toes. There is a fine coating of hair extending to the end of the feet and along the length of the tail. Few people will ever hear a water vole communicate by vocalisation, but chirping sounds 'reminiscent of a house sparrow' have been heard when animals are agitated or as a prelude to mating or fighting. Some communication calls may be beyond the range of human hearing but can be heard on a bat detector.[3]

3) Strachan, *Water Voles (British Natural History Series)* (London: Whittet Books, 1997).

The water vole has a buoyant style of swimming, its body sitting quite high on the water, creating a rounded bow wave.

Water vole eating creeping buttercup leaf.

Common rat. **Photo**: Shirley Freeman.

THE COMMON RAT (*RATTUS NORVEGICUS*)

Brown rat, Norway rat, sewer rat.

The common rat has a much more angular face than a water vole with a long, pointed muzzle and large, prominent ears that have a fine covering of hair. The common rat's pelage is grey-brown above and pale grey beneath. Unlike the water vole, the rat has a much longer tail which is almost the length of the head and body again. It is scaly in appearance and has few hairs. Rats are a lot heavier than water voles, with adults weighing around 500 to 600 grams.

Rats are omnivorous and eat a range of plants, seeds, invertebrates, crustaceans, small mammals, eggs and nestlings. Rats are strong swimmers and are able to dive and swim under water.

part 2

How Water Voles Live

How water voles live

Water voles usually operate within three metres of water along streams, rivers, drainage channels, ditches, small lakes, reservoirs, marshes or ponds. They need suitable earth banks in which to burrow, and deep, slow-moving water where the level does not fluctuate too much. They seem to prefer narrower waterways less than three metres wide, so that they are able to operate on both banks. When they live along major rivers or on upland streams that are liable to rise fast, they are more likely to develop their burrow systems along meanders, which help slow and regulate the flow of water.

Ideal water vole habitat has wide margins of waterside (or riparian) vegetation that provides both a varied food source and a measure of protection from predators. The best sites will have layers of dense, lush vegetation with a variety of plant species at mixed heights, growing both from the water and on the banks. Water voles avoid sections of waterways that are overshadowed by trees as this limits the growth of waterside plants that they need for cover.

Water voles often make use of areas with grass tussocks that provide good cover and that screen tunnel entrances. Traditionally, some of the best places to see water voles in Derbyshire have been along the canals such as the Cromford, Erewash or Chesterfield where they have excavated their burrows behind the canal walls and used the gaps in the stones as their tunnel entrances.

It is becoming more and more difficult to observe water voles owing to their increasing scarcity, but it is possible to look out for signs of their

Dense layers of riparian vegetation alongside deep, slow-moving water provide an ideal habitat for the water vole on the River Bradford.

presence and a guide to what to look out for is featured on page 52.

While most people associate water voles with the streams and rivers of a lowland pastoral landscape, they have been found at over 900 metres in Scotland and in the highest headwaters of Derbyshire's river systems. They can also live along urban streams and rivers that flow through residential or industrial areas.

OPPOSITE PAGE, LEFT: An immense variety of plants growing in and alongside Bradwell Brook – a stream well known for its water voles. TOP RIGHT: A juvenile water vole sits midstream on a mat of weeds. Photo: Hilary Tann. BOTTOM RIGHT: Water vole swimming through broad-leaved pondweed on the Cromford Canal.

Burrows

Water voles live in burrows which are often quite extensive, with interconnecting tunnels, nesting chambers, food storage areas and several entrances. The entrances are at different levels, some below water, some around the water level while others can be quite high up on a steep bank, or on level ground away from the water. The width of the hole is usually four to eight centimetres and it is wider than it is high. The burrow entrances of wood mice and field and bank voles are much smaller, at just two to three centimetres across.

In the autumn, nesting materials are collected and taken down through tunnel entrances to line and insulate sleeping chambers. In spring and summer, nurseries are also constructed underground with finely shredded grasses or reeds.

Water vole outside its extensive and well-worn burrow entrances on the River Derwent.

Often tunnel entrances at the waterline are larger, having been washed away by water and wear. Water voles also create boltholes that are simply an entrance to a short tunnel, with a single chamber at the end. Rats sometimes take over water vole burrows and live in the same territory, but their tunnel entrances are bigger (eight to ten centimetres) with spoil heaps outside, and the ground around them bare with well-worn runs evident.

Water voles excavate their burrows in soft or sandy soil that is sufficiently firm to maintain the tunnel structure. The various levels of their entrances usually allow them to enter or leave the burrow, however high or low the water level is. The top entrances away from the water help to ventilate the burrow, and when a female is nursing young she can make a fast exit or just emerge from the top land hole to graze without leaving the nest. This often results in the appearance of a 'lawn' around the hole. Lower underwater entrances are escape routes from danger, and help to protect the water vole from the invasion of predators. However neither narrow tunnels nor underwater access have deterred the water vole's most voracious predator, the American mink, from invading their burrows.

TOP· Water vole collecting nesting material in autumn.
ABOVE: Rat burrow entrances on the River Amber.

Water voles make use of several burrows, the number per water vole varying according to the occupation density of a watercourse. If there are high densities of voles in suitable habitat, individual water voles use fewer burrows, but with lower numbers they spread out to occupy more burrows. Once animals become more isolated they make less use of multiple burrows, reflecting a reluctance to move around in their territory. There is some evidence that under extreme pressure of predation by mink, water voles in some sites appear to behave differently.

Burrow systems can be seen along watercourses long after water vole colonies have become locally extinct. Holes and runways may persist for years depending on the soil type and conditions. Many of the stream and river banks in Derbyshire are dotted with runs of burrow entrances, but this is no indication of occupation, only of the resilience of the excavated tunnels and entrances. However these lines of holes show where water voles have chosen to live in the past and these areas may well become occupied again. Sites once used by water voles may be recolonised after long periods of absence, as water voles are known to favour historical sites if mink have been eradicated or have moved on.

A burrow entrance in the foreground on top of the bank on Bar Brook is used for ventilation and for quick access. The flat area of vegetation is a 'lawn' grazed by the nursing mother vole. A latrine is evident above the hole at the water's edge.

Burrow entrances at water level and above.

The multi-access holes allow for escape or refuge higher into the bank in times of flood, but it is hard to imagine how populations of water voles can withstand the sudden and dramatic rise in both volume and velocity of the headwaters in upland streams after heavy rain. When the water table is high, and in some wetland habitats, water voles will sometimes build nests on higher ground similar to harvest mouse nests (but much larger), weaving the structure into the base of rushes or reeds. They then line the nest with finely shredded vegetation.

Some colonies of water voles live in reedbeds – an important habitat that provides a degree of safety from predation by mink owing to the non-linear nature of the habitat and the extensive areas of dense cover which are harder for the mink to penetrate. Also the sheer density of vole populations in some non-linear wetlands may ensure a certain level of damage limitation from mink. The targeting of conservation effort in wetland habitats is explored further in Part 7. In marsh and reed habitats, water voles will habitually build above ground nests during the breeding season – a behaviour that is unrelated to high water levels. They then spend the winter in burrows in adjacent banks.[1]

When rivers burst their banks or there is erosion caused by fast flow, water vole burrows are extremely vulnerable; the opposite extreme, drought, also presents problems when rivers and streams dry out – bank sides crumble and the riparian habitat is destroyed.

1) Carter and Bright, 'Reedbeds as refuges for water voles (Arvicola terrestris) from predation by introduced mink (Mustela vison)' in *Biological Conservation*, Vol.111, No.3 (2003).

What water voles eat

Water voles are mainly herbivorous, and feed on large quantities of plant material of which they consume around 80 per cent of their body weight daily. Their main diet consists of the stems and leaves of waterside plants, grasses, sedges and other herbaceous plants. They eat flowers such as pollen-rich pussy willow and water crowfoot – especially during pregnancy – and autumn fruits such as blackberries that grow near to the water. The diet varies considerably with the season, so that in summer almost half of what they consume is herbs, but in winter they depend on more woody material, which then constitutes almost 40 per cent of their diet.[2]

2) Strachan, *Water Voles* (London, 1997), p27.

Water vole at its haul-out platform eating water crowfoot.

Water voles eat the bark and young leaves of waterside trees such as alder, willow, hawthorn and elder in winter and spring. I have watched them clambering on to the roots and lower branches of waterside trees and frequently falling off into the water before resuming the effort to reach some succulent new growth.

By examining feeding remains of water voles from a wide range of sites in a national survey in 1993, researchers Strachan and Jefferies found and listed 32 species of grasses, 7 rushes, 23 sedges, 23 aquatic plants, 104 herbaceous plants and 38 trees (a total of 227 plant species). Water voles have also been known to eat freshwater molluscs, earthworms and small fish. According to a report produced by the Sorby Natural History Society, 'a dead fish nibbled by this species' was found along the Chesterfield Canal in the 1970s. In the 1960s, Stephanie Ryder, who kept pet water voles and wrote a booklet about them for *The Sunday Times*, had one pregnant water vole that devoured five different native species of dead fish. These omnivorous adventures were most likely aimed at providing supplementary protein during pregnancy. In the 17th century Izaak Walton believed that the 'Craber, which some call the Water-rat' was an enemy of the 'poor Fish', but at that time any excuse was used to persecute almost any wild animal.

Water voles can often be seen feeding at the water's edge on 'platforms' that have been worn by use, on rocks or man-made structures such as canal walls, or midstream on beds of water plants where they have dragged out water weeds and semi-emergent plants. The way in which water voles handle and manipulate their food can be a source of quiet entertainment for the observer. Many of the waterside plants selected by water voles are tall, so that once an animal has secured a piece of vegetation it will sit on its haunches in a favoured spot and chomp its way through often considerable lengths of waterweed, reed stem or tall grass.

A water vole will sit and hold its food using its front paws grasping either side of the plant. As each section is cut through by the vole's formidable incisors and chewed by its continuously growing molars, the plant stem is moved up into the vole's mouth and chubby cheeks with the plant eventually disappearing or being discarded. According to Stephanie Ryder the water vole is fastidious about its food and 'can be seen to run the paws briskly down the length of whatever it is he is eating … and shakes each paw before taking hold of a stalk … to remove mud before eating.'[3]

3) Ryder, *Water Voles* (*Animals of Britain no.4*) (London, 1962), p12.

WHAT WATER VOLES EAT

Water vole making use of a tiny island.

As the water vole has to consume around 80 per cent of its body weight daily this requires much foraging, much sitting and much munching. During lactation, a female needs to consume double her weight in vegetation every day.

Water voles seem to follow a four-hourly rhythm of activity and are active above ground for around an hour before going underground for another three. Radio tracking of individuals has shown that far from sleeping, they are still busy underground sorting out their burrows, working on tunnels and chambers and arranging or eating their foodstores.[4]

Through the autumn and winter, water voles spend more time in their burrows and make use of foods collected earlier in the year, which have been stored in chambers and along the tunnels of the burrow. But they also make occasional foraging expeditions to feed on what vegetation may be available, as well as various roots, tubers, rhizomes, bulbs and bark. In the autumn and winter, water voles are less active. They do not hibernate but go into a semi-dormant state to conserve energy.

4) Strachan, *Water Voles*, pp36–37

TOP: Water vole in summer eating grasses in the shallows.
BOTTOM: Water vole eating rhizomes in autumn.

The life cycle of the water vole

The water vole breeding season in England begins in April and ends in September. In Scotland the season is shorter, beginning in May and ending in August. Mating activity starts early in the spring, with males coming into mating condition in late February and females coming into oestrus in March. Over-wintering water voles start to be more active as the days lengthen, and disperse to establish breeding territory. Females that have shared nests over the winter will either compete for territory or disperse to find somewhere new.

Breeding females produce between one and five litters a year, with three being an average number, and an average of five or six young in each litter. The gestation period is 22 days.

Young water voles (called either pups or cubs) are born naked and with their eyes closed, weighing between 3.5 and 7.5 grams (about the same as a level or heaped teaspoon of sugar). They suckle for around three weeks, but make their first forays outside the burrow when they are about two weeks old, which is when weaning starts. At this stage they weigh around 22 grams. They remain in the nest with their mother, sometimes venturing outside to feed, until the next litter comes along. By this time they are at least three weeks old and weigh between 30 and 40 grams. Some young water voles may remain in their birth territory after the arrival of their mother's next litter but they are often driven away by her. The male has no role in raising the pups but Stephanie Ryder had noticed that among her captive water voles the fathers would seem to recognise and gently nuzzle their progeny in passing and even visit small babies in the nest.

Juvenile water voles vary a great deal in the rate at which they grow depending on habitat, food availability and security of territory. Young voles that are born before July will reach physical maturity in the year that they are born, but they need to weigh at least 170 grams if they are to survive the winter. A few water voles from the first litters of the year will be able to breed in their first year.

Few water voles survive two winters, and survival over three winters is very rare in the wild, but some water voles in captivity have lived to this age.

TOP: Water vole pup in April.
BOTTOM: Adult water vole in November.

Two water vole pups at around three to four weeks old.

In common with most wild animals, water voles are often afflicted with parasites such as fleas, lice and ticks, and they can often be seen scratching. They can also carry a form of leptospirosis, or Weil's disease, that can be fatal to humans. Anyone surveying for water voles is fully briefed on the potential biological hazards of contact with water inhabited by either water voles or common rats, which also carry Weil's disease.

Water vole colonies

Most water voles live in colonies strung along lengths of stream, river or ditch which may extend over one or two kilometres. The nature of these colonies is determined by the type and quality of habitat. In ideal habitat such as a deep, slow-moving stream with wide margins of dense riparian plants, there may be large populations of voles concentrated in short stretches of waterway. Where habitat is poor or patchy, colonies may be widely spaced out with uninhabitable territory separating groups, leading to lower densities of more isolated animals. There may be many individually defended territories or 'home ranges' within a breeding colony of water voles. Many occupants of a colony may be related, but individuals will emigrate to neighbouring colonies and incomers will move in. There may be some distance to travel between colonies, which can make dispersal hazardous to those on the move.

Some water voles live in reedbeds or marshy areas, so their home range can be defined as an area of wetland habitat, but most voles live along waterways, so it is usual to measure their occupancy or range using linear measures. Population densities range from 2.4 to 14 water voles per 100 metres of riparian bankside. In reedbed or marshy areas, populations are measured per hectare and may reach quite high densities of up to 50 per hectare.

Populations of water voles living in uplands may be very small and fragmented and are often separated by large distances. Their ability to link up with each other is crucial to their persistence in this habitat.

The monogamous female establishes her territory within a breeding colony and will defend it against intruders but she may share territory with female offspring. Fights between water voles are not uncommon with animals biting and boxing each other and making angry chattering noises. Fighting can lead to fatalities with juveniles being especially vulnerable to aggressive adults. Researchers have found that if population density is high, there is less fighting and there are more overlapping and undefended territories.[5]

The home range for territorial females varies between 30 and 150 metres depending on time of year, quality of habitat and population density. Males are non-territorial with a more extensive home range of 60 to 300 metres in which they move freely between the ranges of several breeding females and those of other males. Mature males remain in the same home range throughout their lives whereas females have to find and defend breeding territories and this may mean travelling some distance from where they were born. Male water voles compete with other males to mate with several females. Larger males with more extensive home ranges have greater access to females and sire more offspring. The ranges of upland dwelling water voles may be greater than the usual distances. Juveniles occupy smaller home ranges than breeding adults.

In the winter, water vole colonies shrink down, home ranges contract and voles no longer hold territories. Many water voles share communal nests and their ranges do not extend very far from their burrows.

5) Telfer, Piertney, Dallas, Stewart, Marshall, Gow and Lambin, 'Parentage assignment detects frequent and large-scale dispersal in water voles' in *Molecular Ecology*, Vol.12, No.7 (2003).

OPPOSITE PAGE: Water vole patrolling its territory along the River Derwent. The greatly enlarged burrow entrance has been worn by water and much use over time.

Dispersal

The survival of populations of water voles depends on successful dispersal so that new areas can be colonised, and where extinctions have occurred these areas can be recolonised. This process depends on the movement of individual water voles. In the spring, adult males and females will begin to move away from territory they have shared with other voles through the winter, in order to breed. At this time the population of water voles is at its lowest and there is ample territory to find or recolonise, but dispersal is sometimes the result of fights after which the loser moves on.

Later in the year, some of the young males and females in a colony will disperse during their first summer. Others will remain close to their natal site (birthplace) as non-breeders until the winter. Most males that are born

early will disperse by the time they are four months old, but if they are younger they will stay close to their natal site. While only a minority of females breed in their first year, territorial fights between mothers and daughters can happen. Juveniles (especially females) are very vulnerable to predation while dispersing.

There are many variations to the patterns of dispersal and distances travelled by individuals, which relate to the size and density of the population and the territory occupied. For example, while dispersal along the Cromford Canal may involve an excursion of a few hundred metres, water voles in the uplands of Bleaklow or Kinder Scout may travel along streams and overland a distance of some kilometres. A study in north-east Scotland in the late 1990s of the rate and scale of dispersal between

Water vole pup (depicted slightly larger than life size).

small subdivided populations of water voles detected one female that had travelled over five kilometres from her natal site.

On the move in early spring.

Latrines

Water vole faeces are 8 to 12 millimetres long and 4 to 5 millimetres wide. They are rounded at each end in a cigar shape. They vary in colour depending on what plant material has been ingested but are often greenish when fresh. If they are broken open when dry they can show concentric circles of plant matter. Rat droppings are larger and foul smelling whereas water vole droppings have no distinct odour. While water vole droppings are round at the ends, rat droppings have at least one pointed end.

Scattered droppings along runways or on rocks close to the water provide important evidence of water vole presence, but a true latrine will have many droppings and may be extensive and show evidence of being trampled down with fresh droppings deposited on top. These may be close to a burrow entrance, at a feeding station or at a boundary that indicates the end of a breeding female's range.

Many mammals scent mark their territories at important sites. Excreta contain a wealth of information that is communicated both to members of the same species and to other species. Scent trails are what guide the predator as well as providing connectivity between populations of mammals. The complex language of olfactory signals can range from information about territory to gender identity and sexual availability.

Water voles make use of their latrines to communicate to other voles about their territory, status within a population and their availability to mate. They maintain their latrines by visiting important sites daily, adding droppings and scent marking. Water voles have scent glands in their flanks, which secrete a thick, waxy, heavily scented substance that coats the surrounding hair. Water voles stroke the gland with their hind feet and then convey the scent to the latrine by drumming with their hind feet on to the pile of droppings. Breeding females hold their territory and mark their range by maintaining about six latrines. Both sexes scent mark their latrines and males will also scent mark females' latrines.

TOP: A grey wagtail on a log where a water vole has left scattered droppings.
BOTTOM: A latrine with a mix of trampled and fresh droppings.

In a study of water vole behaviour in the 1970s, Christine Leuze found that adult males positioned their latrines at the end of their mates' ranges. She found that by removing male voles and artificially maintaining their latrines, individual females stayed confined within those scent-marked boundaries originally created by the males. She also found that by removing these end latrines, females would range beyond their previous territories leading to some fierce fights with neighbouring females.[6] So while the roaming, non-territorial males can wander far, they appear, even while absent, to exert considerable control over territory occupied by their mates.

The mating season gets underway in March, and some building of latrines may begin then. Research has shown that there is a direct link between the number of latrines built, the extent of building activity and the intensity of the mating season. So although the first latrines will normally appear in early March, a cold early spring will delay this. The number and size of latrines will increase through to high summer and into the autumn. But new latrines will not be built or maintained after October. This corresponds exactly with the most intense period of mating and reproduction.

Large trampled latrines provide static evidence of the presence of voles and of breeding activity. They are easy to see as they are often in prominent positions on a waterway and they are important in helping to locate breeding colonies and to estimate numbers of voles within populations.

Water voles are most evident in early spring (despite the low population at this time) when they are seeking out or establishing new territories and when vegetation is low.

6) Leuze, 'Social Behaviour and dispersion in the water vole Arvicola terrestris', (Unpublished PhD thesis, University of Aberdeen, 1979).

Counting water voles

A study was undertaken in 1989 on four rivers in North Yorkshire to find out if the number of latrines and the pattern of their creation linked to water vole abundance.[7] A distinction was made between core sites with latrines and evidence of breeding (both by sightings and signs of juvenile water voles), and peripheral sites. The correlation between numbers of water voles trapped and latrines counted along measured stretches of river was later used as a model for estimating numbers in the first ever national survey of Britain's water vole numbers conducted in 1989–1990 by the Vincent Wildlife Trust. A total of 7,294,000 was estimated as the summer population of water voles in Britain in 1990.[8]

Today, water vole latrines remain our best clue as to the presence and number of water voles on any waterway, but the formula for counting cannot necessarily be made to fit all habitats as some sites could have far higher densities than those studied in North Yorkshire. But the rough guide to numbers in water vole colonies is just one aspect of the valuable data provided by latrines.

7) Woodroffe, Lawton and Davidson, 'Patterns in the production of latrines by water voles (Arvicola terrestris) and their use as indices of abundance in population surveys' in *Journal of Zoology*, Vol.220, No.3 (1990).   8) Jefferies, Strachan and Strachan, 'Estimated numbers of three interacting riparian mammals in Britain using survey data' in Jeffries, ed., *The Water Vole and Mink Survey of Britain 1996–1998 with a history of the long-term changes in the status of both species and their causes* (Ledbury, 2003).

Predators

Water voles have many predators, the most important of which is the introduced American mink but the list of native predators is considerable and includes owls, kestrel, heron, golden eagle (in Scotland), stoat, weasel, polecat, otter, fox, common rat and pike. Domestic cats kill water voles and dogs have also been known to catch and kill them.

Most people who have encountered water voles are familiar with the distinctive 'plop' sound they make when they 'splash-dive' into the water. This is a strategy to warn other water voles of danger and the scent and/or sight of humans is enough to provoke this response. Another tactic used by water voles is a quick churning of the streambed to stir up sediments and muddy the water so that their exit route cannot be seen.

ABOVE: A large pike in the Cromford Canal.
OPPOSITE PAGE, TOP LEFT: Grey heron. BOTTOM LEFT: Barn owl hunting. RIGHT: Male kestrel.

How to see water voles

Water voles are diurnal (active in daylight) and so especially during spring and summer they can be seen feeding, swimming or moving along their trackways through vegetation. They are also active at night, but where rats are present they will avoid encounters with their mainly nocturnal neighbours and this forces the water voles to forage more in daylight.

Early spring is a good time to see water voles even though the population is at its lowest at this time. In spring, vegetation is short and the plants that provide cover have not grown to their full height, but voles still need to spend considerable time out of their burrows in order to satisfy their voracious appetites. They will spend as much as 30 to 40 per cent of the day outside of their burrows during the spring and summer, but the dense growth of waterside plants in high summer makes it very hard to see them moving along their runways or feeding outside concealed burrow entrances.

Early morning and late afternoon are said to be the best times to see water voles, but I have seen them at all times of the day. There is no need to wear camouflage as water voles have poor eyesight, but since they can see movement

it is wise to move slowly, or stay still and keep quiet when one is spotted. They are sensitive to scent, and while they can seem oblivious to quiet human presence, it is advisable to be aware of the direction of the prevailing wind so that you are downwind of the animal(s). Water voles have acute hearing and can be easily disturbed by sudden sounds, and juveniles appear to be the most nervous. However, there are many places in Derbyshire and elsewhere where water voles have become so accustomed to the scents and sounds of humans and dogs that they appear to be undeterred by their presence. Nonetheless, disturbance in the water, particularly by dogs entering it, will drive water voles underground and may drive them away altogether.

People should do everything they can to avoid causing any disturbance or stress to these extremely endangered animals, and remember that they are breaking the law and liable to criminal prosecution if they disturb a 'place which water voles use for shelter or protection'.

The best chance to see them is by scanning banks with binoculars for prolonged periods where there are known colonies of water voles, and learning to detect their presence by knowing the signs to look for.

Cromford Canal near Ambergate in late summer.

FIELD SIGNS

There are a number of ways to discover the presence of water voles.

FOOTPRINTS

Tracks may be evident in mud along the margin of a watercourse. Juvenile rat footprints are similar in both size and arrangement so it is not always possible to confirm the presence of water voles by tracks alone. There are four toes on the forefoot arranged in star shape and the hindfoot has five toes with the outer toes splayed. Tracks lie about 45 millimetres apart and the stride length is around 120 millimetres.

RUNWAYS

Paths are pushed through the vegetation and used to gain access to the water, feeding areas or to burrow entrances. Runways form grassy tunnels through vegetation close to the water and are between five and nine centimetres wide.

BURROWS

Burrows appear as a series of holes in the bank, usually above a watercourse though some are on the waterline. Burrows are usually four to eight centimetres in width. Water vole-sized holes can be misleading, as burrow structures can persist long after they are deserted, and they might be occupied by rats.

LAWNS

Areas surrounding a hole close to the water appear to be grazed short in what are commonly called 'lawns'. The lawns are usually evident around holes on the top of a bank.

FEEDING STATIONS

Water voles have favourite places along their pathways where they can sometimes be seen eating. They often leave the remnants of discarded vegetation which can appear to be cut into neat lengths of about ten centimetres. Sometimes pieces of plant material are bitten into neat lengths and taken down into the burrow as food stores, but often they are left as piles of unwanted remains. On close examination these pieces of vegetation can show the marks

of two large incisors with the cut made at a 45-degree angle. In upland or marshy areas strips of pith (the white core of rushes) can be found where the vole has stripped off the green outer part. Other feeding signs include the cut tops of emergent plants where water voles have been feeding, but the presence of sheep or cattle can make this harder to determine. In wetland habitats where field voles are also present, care needs to be taken in distinguishing the feeding signs and also the droppings of the field vole from the young water vole.

DROPPINGS

Faeces are the most important field sign for water voles. Look for scattered blunt-ended droppings 8 to 12 millimetres long and 4 to 5 millimetres wide, or for extensive flattened down piles of droppings which are latrines. If you find this evidence you know that water voles are present.

OPPOSITE PAGE, TOP LEFT: Water vole footprints. The forefoot has four toes arranged in a 'star' shape while the hindfoot has five toes. TOP RIGHT: Top burrow entrance with grazed lawn.
BOTTOM LEFT: Runway entrance through vegetation at the water's edge. BOTTOM RIGHT: Latrine with feeding signs of discarded pith from soft rush (*Juncus effusus*) that has been stripped by the water vole.

part3

A Protected Species

Water voles and the law

*'My first job was "Slaney, take that .22 rifle and shoot those water voles".
I was 17, I'm 46 now. About 20 years ago the attitude to water voles changed.
The actual thinking was that water voles were causing banks to collapse.'*

The first orders given to Warren Slaney when he was apprentice river keeper on the Haddon Estate reveal the casual persecution of water voles in quite recent times.

In recognition of their dramatic decline, water voles are now fully protected by the law in England and Wales. They had been given some limited legal protection in 1998 when the species was included in Schedule 5 of the Wildlife and Countryside Act of 1981 (as amended). In April 2008, in recognition of the perilous state of the species, water voles gained enhanced protection so that the animal itself, as well as its place of shelter or protection, became fully protected under the provisions of Section 9 of Schedule 5 of the Act.

Natural England and Defra (Department for Environment, Food and Rural Affairs) have outlined the legal position of the water vole (see opposite).

WHAT YOU MUST NOT DO

You are breaking the law if you:

- intentionally capture, kill or injure water voles

- damage, destroy or block access to their places of shelter or protection (on purpose or by not taking enough care)

- disturb them in a place of shelter or protection (on purpose or by not taking enough care)

- possess, sell, control or transport live or dead water voles or parts of them (not water voles bred in captivity).

If you're found guilty of an offence you could be sent to prison for up to 6 months and be fined £5,000 for each offence.

ACTIVITIES THAT CAN HARM WATER VOLES

Activities that can affect water voles include:

- destroying or disturbing their habitat

- destroying or disturbing places used for shelter or protection

- changing water quality.

In most cases you should be able to avoid harming the water voles, damaging or blocking access to their habitats.[1]

1) Natural England and Defra, *Water voles: surveys and mitigation for development projects* [online] <https://www.gov.uk/water-voles-protection-surveys-and-licences>

Water voles live in a wide variety of habitats and, surprisingly, there are a number of colonies in urban areas. They are often much closer to human habitation and to human presence than many people realise. With the level of protection that they currently have, there are often issues arising from human activity that could potentially damage or destroy water vole burrows or damage the animals themselves. The law demands that 'due attention is paid to the presence of water voles and appropriate actions taken to avoid committing offences'.[2]

Defra recommends that local planning authorities seek advice from Natural England or the Environment Agency about planning applications for developments that may affect protected species, and provides so-called 'standing advice' on water voles and a range of other protected species which planning authorities use to help with planning decisions. This requires surveys to be undertaken if records suggest that water voles may be present or if the habitat is suitable for water voles. Following survey, the impacts of planned activities must be assessed and where impacts are identified these must be addressed in a mitigation plan.[3]

This high level of protection has so far produced few prosecutions. It has, however, generated a lot of work for the environmental consultants who carry out the ecological appraisals.

In addition to its protected legal status, the water vole is considered to be a priority species for conservation. In England the current list of priority species is that published by the Secretary of State under Section 41 of the Natural Environment and Rural Communities Act 2006. This Act also confers a 'biodiversity duty' on public authorities, which requires that they show regard for conserving biodiversity in all their actions.

The government's National Planning Policy Framework guides local planning policies and in order to minimise impacts on biodiversity this requires that local authority plans should, among other things, 'promote the preservation, restoration and re-creation of priority habitats, ecological networks and the protection and recovery of priority species populations, linked to national and local targets, and identify suitable indicators for monitoring biodiversity in the plan'.

This requirement, as set out in Local Plans, often makes reference to Local Biodiversity Action Plans, where these are still current.

2) Natural England, *Water voles – the law in practice: guidance for planners and developers* (2008) [online] <http://webarchive.nationalarchives.gov.uk/20140605090108/http://naturalengland.org.uk/ourwork/regulation/wildlife/species/watervoles.aspx>.   3) Natural England and Defra [online], *Water voles: surveys and mitigation for development projects*

Persecution

In Derbyshire, both the Lowland Derbyshire Biodiversity Action Plan and Peak District Biodiversity Action Plan contain detailed targets and strategies to conserve and improve habitat for water voles. Key organisations such as the Environment Agency, Natural England, local authorities, water companies and others are usually partners in Local Biodiversity Action Plans and may have their own separate plans to protect water voles. In short, there are armies out to protect the water vole – at least on paper, that is.

One unforeseen result of the higher protection of water voles has been deliberate persecution – getting rid of them in order to get round perceived constraints on activities caused by their presence as a protected species. Unfortunately, some ruthless people have attempted to eradicate water voles both by destroying or blocking up their burrow systems (which may well be occupied), and by shooting the voles.

Water vole swimming through water crowfoot in July.

Water vole swimming through dense layers of duckweed and water-starwort on the Cromford Canal in October.

Water vole twisting to secure a long stem of water crowfoot.

Water voles are good climbers – this one sits on a branch of willow above the River Wye.

part4

Derbyshire's Water Voles

Derbyshire

Derbyshire sits in the centre of Britain – a medium-sized inland county located in the north of the Midlands. The county has within it a great variety of landscapes that are immensely different in topography, land use and wildlife habitat. An outline of the county's geology, principal features and some nature reserves is given in Appendix 1.

The wild upland regions to the north of the county and low-lying pastoral landscapes of the south are linked by the corridors of the county's river valleys. The hills of the Peak District are the last in the Pennine chain and the county itself embodies cultural and historical links between north and south, upland and lowland. The total area of the county including the city of Derby is 2,625 square kilometres.

Seventy-five per cent of Derbyshire's population lives in just 25 per cent of the land space. The urban and industrial centres with the densest human population are located in the south and east of the county, while the sparsely populated rural areas, including remote upland regions, are mainly in the north and west.

Derbyshire is a place of contrasts, with valleys and open spaces that are worlds apart in feeling and atmosphere, but set apart by just short distances. In his journeys on horseback through the Peak District in the 18th century, Daniel Defoe described the Peak District as a 'howling wilderness' and 'the most desolate, wild and abandoned country in Great Britain'. (Daniel Defoe, *A Tour Thro' the Whole Island of Great Britain*, Vol. 2, 1724.)

In the mid-16th century Charles Cotton recommended the rural idyll to be found on the banks of the River Dove in the south of Derbyshire: 'I promise you nothing can be pleasanter for an artist than the lights and shadows of their umbrageous banks, and the pastures, and the lowing herds by the river, the native cascades and rocks, and the peaceful villages with ancient churches that lend their aid to the composure of those retired prospects.' (Charles Cotton and Izaak Walton, *The Compleat Angler*, Part II by C. Cotton, 1676.)

TOP: The River Derwent at Chatsworth. BOTTOM: East Mill (built in 1912) and North Mill (built in 1804) at Belper are now part of the Derwent Valley Mills World Heritage Site.

The view west from Back Tor on Derwent Edge, with Kinder Scout on the skyline.

Both Cotton and Defoe observed the county before much of it was transformed by the industrial revolution. Coal mining and its associated industries created the need for housing, and for a network of canals to move coal to the growing urban areas. But Derbyshire still has remote, wind-blasted high plateaus, intimate wooded valleys, deep gorges, parklands, open rolling pastures, wide flood plains and an industrial landscape that made the wealth of the county in the past. Much of the old industrial landscape, with its coal mines, cooling towers and brick and iron works, has been transformed into new open spaces for wildlife and for people.

Historical records of Derbyshire's water voles

'Remains of this species have been found, often in large numbers, in the barrows of Derbyshire. At the present time it is found commonly in all our slow flowing streams, but becomes scarcer where the fall is rapid and the bottom stony. Its remains are sometimes, but rarely, found in owl pellets.'
(F.C.R. Jourdain, *The Victoria History of the County of Derby*, 1905.)

There are few historical accounts of the water vole in Derbyshire. The earliest appears in Stephen Glover's *History, Gazetteer, and Directory of the County of Derby* published in 1829. In this he includes a brief mammal fauna of the county in which the water vole is listed as the 'water rat' with no further observation other than a brief description.

Rev. F.C.R Jourdain, the famous ornithologist and naturalist, presented an account of the mammals of Derbyshire in *The Victoria History of the County of Derby*, published in 1905. He noted that the pine marten had gone from the county and the 'polecat bids fair to follow' but rodents fared better as 'the smaller mammals hold their own against man better than their larger relations'. His entry refers to the large number of remains of water voles found in the ancient barrows of Derbyshire. Some possible reasons for the presence of water vole bones found far away from any water in the ancient burial mounds of early Britons are explored in Part 5. However, the most salutary part of his account is the observation that the water vole was present 'in all our slow flowing streams' at the beginning of the 20th century. And a few years later the East Derbyshire Field Club, in its published *Transactions for 1915*, described the water vole as 'common'.

In 1970, Derbyshire Natural History Society published *Derbyshire Natural History: a brief guide*. This very brief guide contains the following entry: 'Water voles, called water rats, although they are not rats but pleasant and harmless animals, are frequent beside ponds, canals and rivers, generally where the stream is not too fast.' While not very informative, this entry confirms the status of the water vole as common in quite recent times. But just how common and widespread they were becomes clearer with a brief but immensely valuable guide called *Mammals of the Derby Area* published in 1969 by Derby Junior Naturalists. This guide was written by John F. Middleton who noted in the introduction that Jourdain's brief work of 1905 had 'remained the most up-to-date systematic review of the county's mammals' for 64 years and that it was time for a 'review of local mammals'. This small and incomplete survey is useful and provides a rough guide to the previous extent of water vole occupation of much of the south of the county.

The entry on the water vole in the 1969 guide is revealing: 'Common and widely distributed. Active by day when it may be observed at close quarters feeding.'

What is most striking about the Derby Junior Naturalists' survey findings is that the greatest extent of their positive records are concentrated in areas now mainly considered to be water vole deserts, that is along the rivers Trent, Dove and Manifold and all around and within the city of Derby. The booklet gives the impression that wherever they looked along rivers, canals, streams, lakes, ponds and ditches they found water voles.

While their findings of mammal presence were recorded in other parts of the county, most of their recording of water vole occupation focused within a ten-kilometre radius of Derby. There are a few records in one-kilometre squares where no watercourse is visible on the 1:50,000 Ordnance Survey map. So perhaps ditches, ponds and canalised watercourses too small to appear on the map in these urban areas were all home to the water vole 45 years ago.

The Sheffield-based Sorby Natural History Society has recorded water voles in parts of north and north-east Derbyshire over many years. In 1980 Sorby published *Mammals in the Sheffield Area*, a report based on six years of fieldwork with over 16,000 records of individual mammals. With Sheffield at the centre of the area surveyed, many records to the south and west were from Derbyshire. The water vole entry reads: 'The Water Vole has a widespread distribution throughout the Sheffield area, associated with most types of still and slow-moving water. It is most common on the well vegetated banks of lowland stretches of water, such as rivers, canals, lakes ponds, ditches, subsidence flashes and streams.' The report notes 'particularly large populations on the Chesterfield Canal'. The authors of the report, Valerie Clinging and

Derek Whiteley, also describe how the water vole was less common in upland areas but 'does inhabit moorland streams and conduits leading to reservoirs'. They were among the first people to notice and record water voles living in this kind of habitat. Sorby subsequently produced an online mammal atlas for 1970–1997 and 1980–2000, where it was noted in 2000 that while water voles were still present in most of its known localities, 'localised declines seem to correlate well with known presence of Mink'.

Our knowledge and understanding of mammals in Derbyshire has increased massively over the last 30 years. In 2012 the Derbyshire Mammal Group and Sorby Natural History Society published a complete Derbyshire mammal atlas – *The Mammals of Derbyshire* – with comprehensive, detailed accounts and distribution maps of 39 mammal species in the county. Written by Dave Mallon, Debbie Alston and Derek Whiteley, and with a foreword by the late Dr Derek Yalden, then president of The Mammal Society, the atlas represented data from over 85,000 records submitted by at least 3,000 observers.

Derbyshire Wildlife Trust holds all of the water vole records for the county previously held by the Derby Biological Records Centre. The records currently cover the period 1925–2015 with around 85 per cent of these collected after 1997, and very few records before 1969. So whatever documented scraps of information can be traced from the past about sites formerly occupied by the water vole can help us to understand not only what we have lost, but also what we might regain. Researchers have found that where water voles once lived they may return, so securing records is vital for future conservation work.

Derbyshire Wildlife Trust survey 1997–1999

The first national water vole and mink survey was conducted by Vincent Wildlife Trust between 1989 and 1990 in order to determine estimated numbers for a baseline by which to compare future findings. This survey was then followed up seven years later, between 1996 and 1998, and showed up such massive losses that a great deal of attention began to focus on the status of water voles all over the country.[1]

Derbyshire Wildlife Trust's survey was launched in June 1997 at the same time as a national 'Water Vole Watch' survey organised by the wildlife trusts. There were several aims to Derbyshire Wildlife Trust's survey:

• To determine the (then) distribution of water voles in the county by a combination of systematic surveys of watercourses and eliciting casual records.

• To assess the extent of any decline by revisiting as many historic sites as possible.

• To increase public awareness of the water vole and its plight, and to involve Trust members and the general public more actively in wildlife recording.

In 1998 a leaflet entitled 'Have you seen a water vole?' was produced in Derbyshire, and across the UK a publicity campaign put the water vole firmly in the public gaze, where it has stayed ever since.

Volunteers were recruited and trained to look for and record water voles and their signs and to note presence of mink and otter along stretches of watercourses that had been occupied by water voles in the past. New territory with suitable habitat was also searched. Three hundred individuals contributed to the survey including members of Derbyshire Wildlife Trust, staff from the National Trust, English Nature, the Environment Agency and Derbyshire County Council's countryside service. Altogether, more than 300 kilometres of watercourses were surveyed by trained volunteers over a period of two years.

Derbyshire Wildlife Trust also received 400 casual records of water voles and their signs between 1997 and 1999.

The Water Vole in Derbyshire report was written for Derbyshire Wildlife Trust by Dave Mallon and Helen Perkins and was published in 1999. This comprehensive survey of the county has provided an invaluable benchmark and resource to inform all the survey work that has taken place in the last 15 years. In addition to the vital data the survey provided, the level of interest and public engagement with the endangered water vole was of immense value. The report describes the response to the survey, which, 'outweighed initial expectations and indicated the positive feelings that the people of Derbyshire have towards the water vole, and their familiarity with the species'.

The rest of this part of the book is an overview of the watercourses of Derbyshire that have been

---

1) The national water vole and mink survey is described in more detail on page 234. What the national survey revealed in the 40 sites it surveyed in Derbyshire (of which 18 were baseline and 22 historical) was that 27.8 per cent of the baseline sites and 81.8 per cent of the historical sites were positive – showing an overall decline of just over 18 per cent. This was well below the national level of decline then estimated to be 80 per cent in just seven years. The extent and nature of those losses is explored further in Part 6.

home to water voles in the past and that may continue to be so in the future. It will refer to the findings of the 1997–1999 survey; monitoring data from 2001–2007 and current data from Derbyshire Wildlife Trust based on staff and volunteer monitoring since 2010; *The Mammals of Derbyshire* (Mallon, Alston and Whiteley, 2012); and my own extensive searches of many Derbyshire watercourses over the past few years.

In recognition of the fragility of water vole populations, this is not intended as a guide to where to find them. Situations change fast, populations fluctuate and extinctions and repopulations occur all the time. Photographs of watercourses represent general areas that water voles have inhabited and all of the photographs of the voles themselves were taken in Derbyshire.

Derbyshire's rivers and their catchments

Map showing the principal towns, rivers and canals of Derbyshire.

Labels on map: WEST YORKSHIRE, GREATER MANCHESTER, Etherow, Glossop, SOUTH YORKSHIRE, Alport, Ashop, Sett, Noe, Peak Forest Canal, Goyt, Buxton, Wye, Bar Brook, Rother, Chesterfield Canal, Chesterfield, CHESHIRE, Derwent, Doe Lea, Lathkill, Bradford, Matlock, Cromford Canal, Amber, STAFFORDSHIRE, NOTTINGHAMSHIRE, Ecclesbourne, Erewash, Ashbourne, Derwent, Ilkeston, Erewash Canal, Derby, Dove, Trent & Mersey Canal, Trent, Swadlincote, LEICESTERSHIRE

This account of Derbyshire's main river catchments and their wildlife mainly goes from south to north, thereby working upstream. Those rivers that flow in from the west and the east are explored in a succession that follows in a northerly direction up the county, apart from the rivers Goyt and Etherow which are in the north-west of the county.

As the Derwent is at the heart of the county and central to the water vole's fortunes we follow it and its tributaries again from south to north. The reason for this – in some ways counter-intuitive – approach is that the decline of the water vole in Derbyshire spread from south to north and it feels better to end the journey with more hopeful signs.

RIVER TRENT

'Others have said, 'tis so called from thirty rivers that fall into it, and there lose their names; which cannot be neither, because it carries that name from its very fountain, before any other rivers fall into it; others derive it from thirty several sorts of fish that breed there, and that is the most likely derivation; but be it how it will, it is doubtless one of the finest rivers in the world, and **the most abounding with excellent Salmon, and all sorts of delicate fish.**'

(Charles Cotton in *The Compleat Angler*, Part II.)

All but two of Derbyshire's rivers ultimately drain south or east into the Trent, and the Trent basin covers much of the Midlands. Whatever the true derivation of 'Trent', Charles Cotton's speculation about the naming of the Trent in 1653 at least demonstrates the health of this major waterway before the industrial revolution.

The Trent is one of the major rivers of England and its third largest, winding its way through most of the Midlands counties before flowing out through the Humber to the North Sea. Much of the industrial and urban development of the Midlands is owed to the Trent and the water quality has suffered in the past from pollution caused by centuries of industrial and agricultural waste. Mineral extraction and drainage has also affected both the flow and health of the main river, with wildlife suffering from these impacts.

The River Trent rises in the Staffordshire moorlands near Biddulph then flows south. North-east of Burton upon Trent it enters Derbyshire and the River Dove joins it at Newton Solney. From thereon the Trent flows in an easterly course through Derbyshire where it runs almost parallel to the Trent and Mersey Canal, which runs from Derwent Mouth near Shardlow to Preston Brook in Cheshire, then linking to the Mersey via the Bridgewater Canal.

Many still associate the Trent with the grime of Midlands industry or the great cooling towers of the power stations that dominated the wide Trent river valley for 50 years. The Trent is now a much cleaner river than it was 50 years ago, and certainly cleaner than it was in the 19th century. An indication of its health is the welcome return of the otter and the continued evidence of its presence in the Trent catchment since 2000. But back in the dirtier days of the late 1960s, the Derby Junior Naturalists recorded water vole occupation in 34 sites in the catchment, including some on the main river and on the Trent and Mersey Canal.

The River Trent near Repton, with the cooling towers of the disused Willington power station in the distance. **Photo**: Kay Thompson.

Now, in contrast, despite several decades of improvement in water quality and the recovery of some wildlife along the Trent, the water vole appears to be virtually absent from the Trent catchment.

The countywide survey of 1997–1999 revisited 75 per cent of previous survey sites and added more sites. Surveyors found evidence of water vole presence in just nine per cent of all the sites. Almost certainly these catastrophic losses were the result of widespread and well-established mink presence. A glance at the map of the Trent's course on page 70 shows how this river and its tributaries at the centre of Britain provide a continuous corridor of waterway from north to south and east to west – a kind of motorway for mink. The expansion of mink into the centre of the country in the mid 1990s was to prove devastating to the water voles in the south and south-west of Derbyshire.

Owing to the lack of volunteer surveyors in the south of Derbyshire, much of the main river has not been surveyed for the last 15 years. So while some local recoveries may have occurred, systematic searches have not been made and neither absence nor presence can be confirmed. However one recent sighting from June 2014 provides a ray of hope as well as grounds for speculation:

'Members of Derby Railway Angling Club were surprised to see "water voles on rafts of floating reeds" floating downstream when fishing on the Trent at Shardlow in June 2014.'[2]

The confluence of the Trent and the Dove at Newton Solney.
Photo: Kay Thompson.

2) Derbyshire Wildlife Trust, *Water for Wildlife* newsletter (2015).

RIVER DOVE

'This river, from its head for a mile or two, is a black water, as all the rest of the Derbyshire rivers of note originally are, for they all spring from the mosses; but is in a few miles travel so clarified by the additions of several clear and very great springs, bigger than itself, which gush out of the limestone rocks, that before it comes to my house, which is but six or seven miles from its source, you will find it one of the purest crystalline streams you have seen.' (Charles Cotton in *The Compleat Angler*, Part II.)

The River Dove rises on Axe Edge Moor near Buxton then flows south for around 45 miles before it reaches the confluence with the Trent at Newton Solney. The Dove forms Derbyshire's western border with Staffordshire.

The Dove flows through some of Derbyshire's most famous and spectacular Carboniferous limestone dales – Dovedale, Wolfscote Dale and Beresford Dale, where Charles Cotton lived at Beresford Hall. The acid water flowing into the Dove is soon neutralised and purified by the limestone through which it flows so that the iconic River Dove still runs for much of its length with clear waters that are classified by the Environment Agency as 'high quality'. A clear testament to this is the continuous record of otter presence since 2000. Currently around half the surveys of the Dove find otter presence.

Chrome Hill and the valley of the upper Dove.

The Dove was, like most of the rivers in Derbyshire, a place where water voles were common and often seen. They were recorded extensively along the Dove and the Manifold in 1969, but by 1997 they had become scarce having gone from 47 per cent of previously occupied sites. There was no continuous distribution of water voles along the upper Dove, and remnant colonies were, according to Staffordshire Wildlife Trust, 'fragmented, small and threatened'. Several casual records were reported to Derbyshire Wildlife Trust in the main tourist areas of Milldale, Dovedale and Beresford Dale.

The countywide survey included results from a catchment survey conducted by the Trent Otters and Rivers Project (OARP). This concluded that most surviving colonies were in the headwaters and minor tributaries of the Dove.

In 2002 a student from Nottingham Trent University, Katie Bates, followed up these findings by resurveying 12 sites in the upper Dove that had been occupied in 1997, as well as some previously unoccupied sites. She found only two occupied sites, and one of these was a new site close to the headwaters of the Dove. What she also found were signs of mink having colonised three of the survey sites. No mink had been detected in 1997. She noted that water voles were absent from sites downstream of these mink occupied areas and concluded that, 'they [mink] may have travelled upstream eliminating water voles as they went'.

The last populations of water voles on the main River Dove appeared to have died out soon after this. However, isolated populations were found during the county survey (1997–1999) on the Henmore Brook near Ashbourne and from four 1-kilometre squares on the large Shirley Brook system. A farmer whose land adjoins the upper Dove near Hartington describes the river as 'infested with mink' along a stretch that she remembers was once heavily populated by water voles.

The regular presence of otters on the Dove may influence the future for water voles for reasons that will become clear in Part 6. River bailiff for the Ashbourne fly fishing club, Mike Gadsby, has caught and killed around 70 mink on the Henmore and Bentley brooks in the last few years. These efforts together with the assiduous trapping and despatching of mink by the river keeper at the Okeover Estate may have delivered results already. According to Derbyshire Wildlife Trust in 2014:

'One individual [water vole] was seen swimming above Okeover weir, and a subsequent survey revealed latrines from a tiny population on the estate.'

Water voles are still present on some of the Dove tributaries. There are water voles present at Carsington Reservoir, which is part of the Dove catchment and where Severn Trent Water together with the RSPB have created extensive and varied wetland habitat around the largest area of open water in Derbyshire. They have been recorded on all of the ponds around the reservoir and in a reedbed at the northern end.

THE EREWASH VALLEY

'The Brangwens had lived for generations on the Marsh Farm, in the meadows where the Erewash twisted sluggishly through alder trees, separating Derbyshire from Nottinghamshire.'

D.H. Lawrence, in his opening to *The Rainbow*, first published in 1915, vividly describes the transformation of this rural backwater in the middle of the 19th century: 'a canal was constructed across the meadows … connecting the newly-opened collieries of the Erewash Valley.' A short time after came the Midland Railway 'and the invasion was complete'. He describes the rapid growth of Ilkeston and the new sounds of the valley, the 'rhythmic run of the winding engines, startling at first, but afterwards a narcotic to the brain … the shrill whistle of the trains re-echoed through the heart … announcing the far-off come near and imminent'.

The Erewash valley is a wetland corridor connecting the Trent valley with the open countryside of Derbyshire. The River Erewash drains the southern part of the coal measures while the River Doe Lea drains the northern part. Forming the boundary between Derbyshire and Nottinghamshire, the Erewash flows south from Kirkby-in-Ashfield, entering Derbyshire at Pinxton whence it flows into the Trent near Long Eaton. Its course through much of Derbyshire is rather inaccessible but the River Erewash and the Erewash Canal are among the most important strongholds of the water vole in the county.

River Erewash with water vole burrows evident in the bank.

The Erewash Canal was built in the late 18th century to take coal out of the Erewash valley pits. It runs for 12 miles between the River Trent, near Long Eaton, and Langley Mill where it once linked to both the Cromford and the Nottingham canals. Both the canal and the River Erewash had numerous records of water vole occupation in the 1997–1999 survey. While some losses were recorded in sites previously surveyed, it was thought that the area had been under-surveyed as 74 per cent of new one-kilometre squares showed signs of water vole occupation. According to the Derbyshire Mammal Atlas, mink 'are noticeably scarce down the eastern border' of Derbyshire and this almost certainly accounts for this area's status as one of the county's water vole strongholds. The Environment Agency commissioned a survey along the River Erewash in 1997 in which findings were recorded along twenty-three 600-metre sections of the river. Surveyors found evidence of water vole habitation in 19 of these sections.[3]

Erewash Meadows is a Derbyshire Wildlife Trust reserve and part of the large floodplain, grasslands and wetlands in the Erewash Valley. A survey of the meadows in 1999 found thriving populations of water voles in many areas adjacent to the river.[4]

Recent Derbyshire Wildlife Trust data maps of Derbyshire watercourses show that the Erewash valley (which follows the eastern county border) has had high numbers of positive records of water vole presence across three 5-year periods. Alarmingly, a fourth map showing all positive records from 2000 to 2014 as blue dots, is overlaid with an almost continuous line of red dots down the eastern border signifying absences recorded between 2010 and 2014. However, results of surveys undertaken by teams of volunteers cannot be said to be definitive as there are so many variables. Water voles may be over-represented in some areas that have been well surveyed, while other areas that are empty of blue dots may not have been surveyed for decades.

3) Baker, Shepherd and Gillespie, *Environment Agency River Erewash Water Vole Survey* (1997).   4) Dean, *Erewash Meadows Nature Reserve: Water Vole Survey. A report to Derbyshire Wildlife Trust and Nottinghamshire Wildlife Trust* (1999).

The Erewash valley has been the subject of intensive surveying activity in the past and despite the alarming picture painted by surveys over more recent years, this remains an area that provides good habitat. The narrow river forms tight meanders through the flood plain creating a deep, slow-moving waterway surrounded by quiet grasslands. These features make this ideal water vole territory.

A stream in the marshy Erewash valley feeds the main river.

The associated canals and wetlands with their dense riparian plants provide extensive linked habitat for the water vole, and the work undertaken by the Derbyshire Wildlife Trust and the Environment Agency has improved water quality and secured this valley as a haven for wildlife. For now much of the Erewash valley has returned to what D.H. Lawrence described as 'the sunny valley where slow water wound along in company of stiff alders'. However, it appears that one proposed route for High Speed Rail (HS2) through Derbyshire might carve its way through part of the Erewash valley and run alongside and over the river with unknowable consequences as the once far-off plan becomes 'near and imminent'.

Pinxton Canal, which supports a strong population of water voles.

Water vole looking out from willow above the water.

THE IDLE CATCHMENT

The magnesian limestone plateau that lies to the east of the coal measures is a predominantly dry area owing to the porosity of the bedrock. The plateau's two rivers, the Poulter and the Meden, flow into the Idle.

The records for water voles are limited in this area, but they are known to occupy the stream that runs into Cresswell Crags. A thriving colony of breeding water voles was found for the first time in 2014 in a newly regenerated fenland site near Bolsover owned by Derbyshire County Council.

The Derbyshire Wildlife Trust survey has numerous records of water voles in the Rother and Idle catchments. These populations appear to have persisted until very recently, but according to more recent data from Derbyshire Wildlife Trust, losses appear after 2010. It is possible that this coincides with the presence of mink in north-east Derbyshire.

Chesterfield Canal with the town's crooked church spire in the distance.
OPPOSITE PAGE: River Rother as it flows through Chesterfield.

RIVER ROTHER AND CHESTERFIELD CANAL

The River Rother rises at Pilsley near Clay Cross and flows first west and then north through Derbyshire, passing through the centre of Chesterfield to feed the Chesterfield Canal. The canal once ran for 46 miles from Chesterfield to the Trent. There are now four miles of water running through the Derbyshire section of the canal, which is an important site for water voles. The Chesterfield Canal's restored towpath is one of the most accessible places to see water voles in the county.

The Rother and its tributary the Doe Lea drain the northern part of the Derbyshire coal measures. The Rother is joined by various streams and by the River Hipper, which rises on the Eastern Moors. The Rother then flows through Rother Valley Country Park – an area formerly in Derbyshire until boundary changes in the 1970s made it part of South Yorkshire. It flows through parts of Sheffield and joins the River Don at Rotherham.

The Rother and the Doe Lea have been heavily polluted in the past by 150 years of coal mining, the untreated sewage outflow from mining communities and chemical pollution from mining's associated industries. Large volumes of solids containing arsenic, cyanide and many other toxic substances were dumped in the river system. In the 1970s the Rother was the dirtiest of many dirty rivers flowing into the Don – the river that was the driving force of Sheffield, the birthplace of steel. Water voles have persisted for years in large numbers in these contaminated areas. The report of Derbyshire Wildlife Trust's 1997–1999 survey commented that, 'Several of the watercourses in this catchment support what appear to be strong colonies of water voles.' A survey undertaken by consultants Baker, Shepherd and Gillespie in 1998 for the Three Valleys Project found evidence of water vole occupation in all of the twelve 600-metre stretches they surveyed on the rivers Drone, Rother and Doe Lea, and Barlow Brook.[5]

5) Baker, Shepherd and Gillespie, *The Three Valleys Project Water Vole Survey* (1998).

THE POST-INDUSTRIAL LANDSCAPE OF NORTH-EAST DERBYSHIRE

It is hard to believe that the extensive areas of wetland habitat, woodland, reclaimed pastures, country parks, nature reserves and nature trails of north-east Derbyshire were once the wastelands left behind after pit closures in the 1980s and 1990s. Alan Heeley is an ex-miner turned ranger who has witnessed the transformation and whose story mirrors that of the landscape he grew up in.

'It was really hard times. When I first started at Markham there were over 3,000 men working there. Every other pit in the local area closed down, so we're talking about tens of thousands of men losing their jobs. It was frightening and exciting at the same time. Markham was one of the last pits to close but I could see what was coming. I left, and 12 weeks later I'd got a job on the railway based at Belper. This was brilliant for wildlife. I only got into wildlife during the strike of 1983–1984 because I had time on my hands. While I was at the pit I had become a part-time countryside ranger working every other Sunday. I'm self-taught. I joined the library because it cost nothing and I read up on things and started taking

an interest. In the last 25 to 30 years I've gone from knowing nothing to leading guided walks.'

Iaian Stafford also works as a ranger in north-east Derbyshire for the county council's countryside services. Like Alan, he is a local man who is passionate about his role in creating landscapes for the future, enhancing wildlife habitat and educating and engaging local communities. His job covers an immense area of post-industrial land from the north Derbyshire coal measures to the rich farmland of the magnesian limestone plateau.

'You look at the historical maps around here and you had all the pits and the associated industries; the railways, brickworks and coking plants. There was a coking plant at Wingerworth and another one down at Shuttlewood. There were deep tar pits and that's all going through reclamation, so that Grassmoor Country Park will become twice the size in a while. These have gone from being black areas with mounds of spoil, to being a green part of the county and we have large areas of public access and areas for nature

TOP: Iaian Stafford, county council ranger in north-east Derbyshire.
BOTTOM: Common darter on purple loosestrife.

82

conservation developed in these country parks. You're trying to encourage people to come in to these green spaces, and at the same time you're trying to manage in such a way that whatever conservation value you've got in these sites is always protected. It's a double-edged sword sometimes. We do try and discourage public use where we have ground nesting birds. But we're not like some other conservation organisations, which can segregate parts of the site off. You can't really do that on public land.

'Some of the ponds have got conservation status for their dragonflies. We have got lots of plantation woodland, which will develop over time and become important. I quite like that about the job because you're shaping what these woods are going to be like in the future. We've done an awful lot of grassland restoration. Because of the industrialisation of the land, the grasslands especially are very nutrient poor so we're starting with a very good base with which to make a wildflower meadow. Now we have some of the best and most extensive wildflower meadows in the county.'

ABOVE LEFT: Reed warbler. **ABOVE RIGHT**: Common hawker laying her eggs. **TOP RIGHT**: A pond in Peter Fidler Reserve developed from one of the lagoons known as 'flashes' caused by coal-mining subsidence. **BOTTOM RIGHT**: Reedbeds adjoining the River Doe Lea in Peter Fidler Reserve near Bolsover.

RIVER DOE LEA

The Doe Lea rises near Tibshelf and flows north just east of the M1 motorway. It feeds two lakes at Hardwick Park, which have been home to water voles in the past. The Doe Lea is joined by various streams before passing through a series of lakes west of Bolsover, which are now part of Carr Vale Nature Reserve run by Derbyshire Wildlife Trust. For much of its course the river has been straightened and canalised and has been little more than a drain for industrial effluent and sewage.

North of the river is the Peter Fidler Reserve managed by Derbyshire County Council. There are various small nature reserves near to Bolsover and the river still runs past the Coalite Chemicals site that closed down in 2004. Further north, the Doe Lea is joined by Pools Brook where the Poolsbrook Country Park (the site of former Ireland Colliery) has extensive lakes and ponds. The Doe Lea joins the Rother south of Renishaw.

The production of smokeless fuels increased massively after the Clean Air Act of 1956, thereby improving the air quality of northern industrial of cities such as Sheffield. The massive coking plant at Bolsover, run by Coalite Chemicals, extracted toxic liquors (tar) out of the coal and produced other industrial chemicals by distilling these liquors at a chemical works on the site. The liquors removed from the coal were full of ammonia, and other by-products of various industrial processes were added to the toxic mix. Effluent from the plant was treated by an 'activated sludge process' before being discharged into the River Doe Lea. Unsurprisingly, the River Doe Lea once had the dubious distinction of being called 'the most polluted river in Europe'.

According to MP Dennis Skinner in a statement to the House of Commons in 1992, the river had 1,000 times the safe levels of dioxins. In 1993, Greenpeace examined chemical residues on the Coalite site and took evidence from local farmers, residents and workers in a detailed report in which

River Doe Lea, once described as 'the most polluted river in Europe', now supports many wild creatures, including kingfishers – one of which was seen just before this photograph was taken.

it claimed that Coalite Chemicals was responsible for 'the worst case of dioxin contamination ever found in the UK. Dioxin, one of the most deadly synthetic chemicals known to man, has polluted land, air and rivers around Coalite's Derbyshire plant. Farmers were banned from selling their milk and meat because of the contamination and there have been health scares among local residents.' Greenpeace, *The Poison Factory: the story of Coalite Chemicals* (1993).

TOXIC EFFECTS

As the Derbyshire Wildlife Trust survey report noted in 1999, 'the potential effects of minewater on water voles are unknown and could be subject of research'. I do not know of any such research, however, what we do know is that mink, which are higher up the food chain than non-carnivorous species, are exposed to greater levels of toxins which 'bioaccumulate' in their body tissue. Mink are known to be affected by dioxins, and in particular polychlorinated biphenyls (PCBs), which are persistent, bioaccumulative, toxic contaminants in the environment. Mink were a species chosen to examine the toxic effects of chemicals that occur in polluted environments in the USA.

Extensive research with lab animals at Michigan State University revealed that 'mink are among the most sensitive species to TCDD [tetrachlorodibenzo-p-dioxin] and that they can serve as a valuable model to study the impact of environmental dioxins on carnivorous mammalian species'.[6]

If mink are unable to breed where these pollutants occur it may be that north-east Derbyshire with its poisoned ground and waters has protected water voles from their deadliest enemy until now.

'The water quality in the River Doe Lea seems to be recovering. Peter Fidler was the spoil heap for Bolsover Colliery but now it is one the best sites in the county for grass snakes. We have done work in there for them and I've seen over 20 in a day before now.'
IAIAN STAFFORD

Grass snake.

---

6) Hochstein, Aulerich and Bursian, 'Acute Toxicity of 2,3,7,8-tetrachlorodibenzo-p-dioxin to mink' in *Arch. Environ. Contam. Toxicol.*, Vol.17, No.1 (1988).

Kingfishers now work the river and the wetland sites close by are rich in biodiversity with reedbeds and lagoons that are host to such species as reed and sedge warbler as well as many dragonflies and damselflies. These places are full of life with evolving ecosystems and unusual species. But as the water quality has improved, mink have established a foothold in north-east Derbyshire.

'The mink have come in now and we're actively trying to trap them. We had a sighting on the Doe Lea a few years ago and we ended up with eight or nine which we managed to trap in one trapping session – probably a male, female and kits. There's been a constant trapping effort on the Chesterfield Canal where we know we've got a good population of water voles. We're getting reports of mink in many different areas. We can only trap on our own sites, and as we have to check the traps every day, we can't trap on other people's sites; we haven't got the resources for that. At the moment we have traps out at Pinxton and Williamthorpe, which are long distances apart and we have many other duties to do. Otters help because they displace mink but this catchment in the north-east is probably the last one in the county having otter come in.'
IAIAN STAFFORD

Water voles are still present on the Chesterfield Canal, in various country parks, fishing ponds and some of Derbyshire Wildlife Trust's reserves and local nature reserves, but it appears that these populations are becoming more fragile.

Too often the recreational needs of people are in conflict with the needs of wild creatures but it seems that the interests of the fishing community can benefit water voles. Iaian Stafford explains how managing ponds and small lakes for coarse fishing clubs can help in protecting water vole habitat:

'We are sympathetic in the way that we manage sites for water voles and we try not to disturb them when we're putting in fishing pegs (wooden platforms). We have areas that we don't mow and where we encourage the fishermen not to mow. When a bank is assigned as a fishing area it really helps water voles as having the fishermen on the bank we have less disturbance from other users. Water voles use the area underneath the fishing pegs as a refuge as well. Water voles are quite adaptable creatures really. It's just a case of trying to give them a little foothold. We are managing the amenity for fishermen and trying to educate people to leave certain areas that are for the wildlife. The fishermen at Pinxton are really quite proud that they've got water voles on their site.'

Fishermen can act as guardians and custodians of the banksides, but a minority regard this protected species as a threat to their activities. Iaian says:

'You can find water burrow entrances that have been filled in. Somebody's done that, but we can't prove who's done it.'

OPPOSITE PAGE, TOP LEFT: Kingfisher. TOP RIGHT: Water vole.
BOTTOM LEFT: Reed warbler. BOTTOM RIGHT: Common frog.

The regeneration of post-industrial sites demonstrates how resilient nature is and how areas that have been dealt the blows of environmental pollution, mass redundancies and social deprivation can become wildlife sanctuaries and places to inspire.

'I've seen the changes, particularly at Williamthorpe where nearly a million trees have been planted at the old colliery site. There were slag heaps and now we've got fields of orchids. The names Holmewood and Heath give us a clue to what the area was like before the mines. It was a barren landscape of the pit tip. I can just remember how we used to have all the coal tips and there were these small lagoons where you'd get wading birds. Nestled in between the mining areas you'd get farming as well and there were a lot of hedgerows. We've created a different kind of nature. Because it was a pit tip, the land was high up and now we have developed areas to make it look the way it was long ago. We have got little ringed plovers, redshanks and other waders breeding there. It just takes time. In the end, if you give nature time, it does come right. My top experience in doing this job was seeing lapwing and ringed plover chicks running about on something that I'd created. I'd developed the area, monitored the water levels and got the shallow pools just right. Then to have these little chicks there and a couple of butterfly species that we'd never had before, was a great experience for me.

'I've been lucky enough to see these green spaces grow and through my keeping of a day-to-day diary and general observations I can see that it's got a hell of a lot better. We're managing for future generations. There's some work I'm doing that I'll never benefit from. I hope my granddaughter will benefit from it maybe, but it may be two or three genera- tions on. A lot of people don't really know and appreciate what they have on their doorstep. These places are priceless.'
ALAN HEELEY

The proposed High Speed Rail (HS2) routes through north-east Derbyshire involve diverting a section of the River Erewash and building bridges, viaducts and embank- ments through the floodplains of the Erewash, the Rother, the Doe Lea and the Amber. The footprint of this development could extend across great swathes of this recovered landscape. The spiralling costs of HS2, a project aimed at saving minutes on a train journey, do not take account of the cost of losing green spaces and wildlife habitat that have taken decades to establish.

Female banded demoiselle damselfly.

Errwood reservoir in the Goyt valley. It is easy to see why most reservoirs are unsuitable for water vole habitation as bare banks are revealed when water levels drop in summer.

THE RIVERS OF NORTH-WEST DERBYSHIRE – THE GOYT AND THE ETHEROW

The rivers Etherow and Goyt are the only rivers in Derbyshire that flow to the west coast and into the Irish Sea as part of the Upper Mersey Basin. All the other rivers of Derbyshire flow into the Trent and thence to the Humber and the North Sea. These two rivers start their courses in the high moorland of the north-west corner of the Dark Peak.

RIVER GOYT

The Goyt starts its course on the moors west of Buxton near the Cat and Fiddle pub. It then flows in a northerly direction feeding the two reservoirs in the upper Goyt Valley before flowing through Whaley Bridge to join the Etherow near Marple in Greater Manchester. Before 1997 there were records of only two 1-kilometre squares occupied by water voles along the river, but no signs were found along the Goyt in the 1997–1999 survey. One of the feeder streams, the Black Brook, was the only site found to be occupied by water voles in the Goyt catchment in the 1997–1999 survey. The Peak Forest Canal was formerly home to the water vole but none have been reported there since 1997. Mink were reported in the area in the late 1990s.

RIVER ETHEROW

The River Etherow is situated in the northernmost corner of Derbyshire and descends through the spectacular Longdendale valley. It flows in a south-westerly direction feeding a six-mile chain of five reservoirs near Glossop. The reservoirs – Bottoms, Rhodeswood, Torside, Valehouse and Woodhead – were built in the latter half of the 19th century to provide fresh water for Manchester and Salford. Generally speaking, the Victorian reservoirs were not constructed in a way to make them good wildlife habitats. The steep reinforced banksides, lack of shoreline vegetation and loss of water in summer makes them unsuitable for water voles. Nonetheless, a new site was found at the head of Torside reservoir in 1999 and signs were found in rushes at the head of Woodhead reservoir.

Before the survey of 1997–1999, there had been no systematic searches for water voles in this upland area. The survey recorded the presence of water voles in 19 new one-kilometre squares, most of which were in the upper Etherow and other moorland tributaries. Evidence of water vole occupation was found high on the watershed of the Bleaklow plateau, with just short distances between catchment streams for both the Derwent and the Etherow. Between 2001 and 2007 Derbyshire Wildlife Trust monitored Derwent and Etherow catchment headstreams, pools, drainage ditches and reservoir leats. Hundreds of positive signs of habitation were recorded, with data from some monitoring sites in this area showing that populations appeared to fluctuate over the years, but that events such as mink incursion or high rainfall could have devastating impacts on populations.

Ladybower reservoir can be seen when looking west from Derwent Edge.

THE DERWENT CATCHMENT

'Little flowery fields of every shape and size, square fields, triangles, fish-shaped fields with odd corners, rhomboids, bounded by green hedgerows and black walls, linked arms and ran up hill and down dale, round the folded hills out of sight into countless valleys beyond where the sun set.'

Alison Uttley, *The Country Child* (London, 1931).

The Derwent runs through the centre of Derbyshire and unites the rugged open country of the Dark Peak with the wooded valleys, water meadows, and rolling hills of the central and southern part of Derbyshire. The name 'Derwent' comes from the Celtic 'a valley thick with oaks'. There are still extensive ancient woodlands along the valley. Where Alison Uttley lived in the lower part of the Derwent valley, sloping fields and ancient woodlands descend to the floodplain of the river that had once powered the factories in Arkwright's mills upstream in Cromford.

The Derwent rises at Swains Greave on the north-east slopes of Bleaklow, high in the Dark Peak moors to the west of Sheffield. It then flows south for 66 miles almost entirely through rural landscapes before joining the River Trent at Derwent Mouth near Shardlow, south of Derby. This last stretch through the city of Derby is the only truly urban setting for the River Derwent in its winding course through the county. The Derwent catchment accounts for almost half of the county's land space and its tributaries in the Peak District are some of the best-known rivers in Derbyshire. This exploration of the Derwent's water voles begins in the south of the county taking in some of the main catchment rivers and streams and goes in a roughly northerly direction towards the wildest parts of upland Derbyshire.

LOWER DERWENT FROM DERBY TO MATLOCK

Quite shockingly, it appears that Derbyshire Wildlife Trust has received just one positive water vole record on the main River Derwent south of Matlock since 2010. This solitary dot appears at Belper. Taken together with the apparent absence of water voles on the Trent and most of the Dove and its catchment, the water vole may well be almost extinct in the south-west of Derbyshire, but unless we can invest time, money and volunteer effort in further survey work, we will never know the truth of what the stray dots tell us. Water voles are still present on the Cromford Canal, but the stretch of the Derwent that runs parallel to it (with the A6 and railway dividing their course for much of the way), from Cromford to Ambergate, has no sign of water vole presence after extensive surveying efforts.

RIVER ECCLESBOURNE

The River Ecclesbourne flows for nine miles from Wirksworth to Duffield where it joins the Derwent. The Ecclesbourne valley has been the focus of a pilot project aimed at improving the water quality of this lowland rural river catchment. It was one of 25 catchments in England in a national project to trial a partnership approach to catchment management. The county and district councils, land owners, farming representatives,

The Derwent flowing over the horseshoe weir at Belper.

Environment Agency, Severn Trent Water and Derbyshire Wildlife Trust worked together on an action plan for the Ecclesbourne. Water voles have been locally extinct on the Ecclesbourne for several years but other species have persisted on the river:

'The Ecclesbourne River supports a variety of wildlife including protected species such as white-clawed crayfish, otter and bullhead, as well as other iconic species like brown trout, dippers, mayflies and kingfishers. These face many challenges as a result of human activity in the valley, the main ones being pollution, sedimentation, invasive species and physical obstructions such as weirs, all of which have a significant impact.' The Ecclesbourne Restoration Partnership, *An Improvement Plan for the River Ecclesbourne and its Valley* (2013).

As part of the catchment management project, Derbyshire Wildlife Trust undertook two years of erosion control work and habitat improvement as well as educational work in local schools. Severn Trent Water upgraded sewage treatment to improve water quality for wildlife and the Environment Agency worked with farmers in restricting cattle access to the river by fencing and installing drinking troughs. They also improved the river's flow by removing a weir and with other restoration work.

Local community groups created the Ecclesbourne Way footpath and the Duffield Millennium Meadow nature reserve. Teams of local and Derbyshire Wildlife Trust volunteers as well as the river's three fishing clubs have also worked long and hard at pulling out Himalayan balsam. Further restoration and habitat-improvement work is planned on the Ecclesbourne and it is possible that water voles may yet return here.

FROM GORSEY BANK, SPRINK WOOD, SHE WENDS
TO TURNDITCH, DUFFIELD, INTO DERWENT, TRENT,
HUMBER, NORTH SEA, THE CYCLE FOLLOWS
IN THE DARK, IN THE DEEP
WHERE THE ECCLESBOURNE FLOWS …

WALKERS AND FISHERMEN, DOWN BY THE WATER,
CATTLE AND TROUT, AND BRING BACK THE OTTER —
IF WE LOOK AFTER SMALL RIVERS, LARGE RIVERS GROW
IN THE DARK, IN THE DEEP
WHERE THE ECCLESBOURNE FLOWS

© MATT BLACK, DERBYSHIRE POET LAUREATE, 2011–2013

RIVER AMBER

The River Amber rises close to the village of Ashover in north-east Derbyshire and flows south-west into Ogston Reservoir – a place well known to local bird watchers with over 200 species having been recorded there. The upper Amber was formerly occupied by water voles and there have been recent reports of them there. The Amber flows south from Ogston through Wingfield Park before turning in a westerly direction at Pentrich to join the Derwent at Ambergate. There have been some positive water vole records on the lower Amber but I have seen rats occupying what were once water vole burrows at Amber-gate. The Amber is the Derwent's only major tributary flowing in from the east. The linked watercourses of the Amber, the Derwent and the Cromford Canal provide possibilities for water voles to recolonise but only if rigorous mink controls are in place.

PRESS BROOK'S WATER VOLES AND THEIR GUARDIANS

'We were sitting out the back and a water vole came up out of the stream and walked across the patio in front of us and didn't taken the slightest bit of notice of us.'
LU NOLAN

'They seem to be almost tame. They're not frightened of humans, not like rats are. A water vole just sits there and munches away and you can get very close to them but I've never managed to pet one yet.'
JIM GREEN

Press Brook rises on the east-facing slopes of the foothills below Stonedge. The brook feeds two small reservoirs before descending through farmland to Clay Cross, flowing south where it joins the River Amber at Ogston. This small stream runs through the Brookfield mobile home park near

Clay Cross where it supports a small but much-loved colony of water voles. Lu and Barbara Nolan and Jim and Janet Green are close neighbours who feel very protective of the water voles that live at the bottom of their gardens. They understand how privileged they are to share living space with such increasingly rare animals and all four of them keep a regular lookout for their voles.

'It's uplifting to see the water voles. First thing in the morning I come into the lounge and look straight across at the stream. We do look every day, so it's just part of everyday life. You're just constantly checking to see in the spring when we see the first one and we think, "they're still there", because we've had some really severe winters and we didn't think they'd survive them. They have done, though there aren't as many as there used to be. We cultivated the opposite bank as a little extension to our garden but since we've known about the water voles we leave it alone. So it's gone back to a meadow type of environment, which gives them protection.'
BARBARA NOLAN

'We do get sparrowhawks and other predators, so the water voles need the protection of the undergrowth. Sometimes you only know they're there when you see the vegetation moving. Last October saw quite a lot of tree felling round the bank area and we were very concerned as to what effect this would have on the vole population. I don't think the farmer was aware until last year that there were water voles down here. I would love to see him getting more involved in looking after the water voles and enhancing their prospects by making their habitat better. If we're not careful, they're going to go altogether. We've got an absolutely beautiful situation. It's wonderful to be able to have our own little habitat and we leave it alone. But the problem is getting the farming community to realise just how important it is to take care of the water voles. It's only because of the way that we feel about them that they're here at all. We're all getting older and someone may move here that has no interest in wildlife and that will be the end of the voles. We would like to see them stay and flourish.'
LU NOLAN

'They definitely used to be a lot more common. They used to be from one end of the brook to the other and now you're lucky to see them. We see them almost every day but it's a case of just standing there and waiting. We love them. We feel very protective of them. We've been trying to get the farmer to sell us this little triangle of land opposite our garden. If we could buy it we would just leave it for the water voles. A lot of people on here want nice tidy banks. Ours probably looks untidy but that's what water voles like. Anybody else would probably go across with a strimmer and strim it down to the bare soil. We've had to consider this. If we moved then probably the water voles would go as well.'
JANET GREEN

'We've actually got people here that took their lawns out and put down AstroTurf because it's easier to maintain. The countryside is untidy. If you want wildlife you've got to put up with a bit of mess. We have got to look after the countryside. It feeds us after all, doesn't it?'
JIM GREEN

It is possible that this colony is isolated and therefore doomed, but the water bodies close by the Rother to the east, the Amber to the south and west and various ponds and reservoirs may all support small colonies that are within dispersal distance.

'Who would've thought you would get water voles near Clay Cross? Sometimes it's the heavily protected places like Cromford Canal where they get hammered. What we need is lots of little protected places. If something wipes out a neighbouring pocket then these might survive and join up with others. Whereas if they're all in one place, even if it's heavily protected, it only takes one mink or some other problem to wipe the lot out. So I think that these little pockets are as important, if not more important than the bigger ones.

'Water voles love apples. I saw a water vole that had got an apple that was nearly as big as its head. It had got it in its mouth and it was paddling downstream. It's little things like that that I will remember for the rest of my life. How many people have seen that? And it's on our doorstep. Little things like that make your life better. My life is enriched for seeing a kingfisher or a water vole.'
JIM GREEN

LEFT: Press Brook, a tributary of the Amber, as it flows through the garden of Jim and Janet Green near Clay Cross.
ABOVE: Water vole footprints at the water's edge.

CROMFORD CANAL

The Cromford Canal is one of the best-loved watercourses in Derbyshire. It is situated in the Derwent Valley Mills World Heritage Site, and attracts large numbers of visitors all year round who are interested in the industrial, as well as the natural, history of the area. The canal was built in 1794 and is nearly 15 miles long, joining the Erewash Canal at Langley Mill. The water no longer runs the entire length of the canal as there are derelict and dried out sections to the south, but the northern section is a very important wetland area in the Derwent valley and has for many years been one of the best places to see water voles in Derbyshire. The entire five-mile length of the northern section of the canal from Cromford Wharf to Ambergate is a Site of Special Scientific Interest (SSSI) and the southern two-mile stretch from

Whatstandwell Bridge to Ambergate is a Local Nature Reserve which is managed jointly by Derbyshire Wildlife Trust and Derbyshire County Council. Rare species can be found here including grass snake and water vole.

In summer, the canal's margins are stacked high with a rich variety of plants like meadowsweet, hemp-agri-mony and water mint as well as dense patches of rushes and reeds and the air above the canal is alive with insects including dragonflies and damselflies. Either side of the canal, woodland, scrub and meadow provide ideal habitat for many species of birds including such summer visitors as blackcap, whitethroat, willow warbler, chiffchaff and spotted flycatcher, which thrive on the rich insect life of the canal and its margins. Where there is no tree cover, the dense and varied layers of vegetation

and static water make this optimum water vole habitat. The Cromford Canal has always been regarded as one of Derbyshire's last strongholds for the water vole. Photographers come from miles around to get the perfect shot, equipped with tripod and long lens and often staking out a hole in the bankside or canal wall. Sometimes quite a crowd will gather to photo-graph a nicely performing water vole.

TOP: Little grebe, or 'dabchick'.
BOTTOM: A family of mute swans on the Cromford Canal.

CROMFORD CANAL'S DISAPPEARING WATER VOLES

Sadly though, according to Derbyshire Wildlife Trust, there have been no reports of water voles at Cromford Wharf since 2013. From the whole of the northern section, in the spring of 2014 surveys and reports from the public were 'mostly normal', but from July to December, seven surveys showed no signs of water voles. In the previous year there had been 25 records over the same period.[7]

Shirley Freeman is a familiar sight along the Cromford Canal. Having worked for the Post Office as a general finance manager for over 34 years, she took a degree in natural sciences in 2005 and indulged her lifelong passion for wildlife conservation by becoming a Derbyshire Wildlife Trust volunteer water vole surveyor. She began surveying a short stretch of the Cromford Canal in 2006 and within 12 months surveyed the whole of the five-mile stretch of the Cromford Canal from High Peak Junction to Ambergate. She has many other watercourses that she surveys regularly as well.

'I was brought up near the Chesterfield Canal in the 1950s and Mum always used to take us down at the weekends. There were lots of water voles in the canal and lots of grass snakes. It was just wonderful. We couldn't wait to see the water voles. We had a little Collins pocket book of all the plants and animals and we used to record what we'd seen. So the passion has always been there.

'Water voles are just gorgeous. They've got sweet little faces. They're vulnerable, quite secretive as well sometimes. They are just wonderful. I love them. I love all rodents actually — even rats.

'I'm down here at least once a week. Sometimes its four or five times a week. If they're doing any work such as dredging I'm down here every day, just keeping my eye on them and watching what they're doing which is sometimes needed.

'The autumn habitat management was different last year. Usually the vegetation is left for approximately 25 metres, then strimmed for 25 metres. Last year for some reason half the bankside vegetation was strimmed for 50 metres with 50 metres left standing. If the water voles had happened to be using the strimmed section they would have moved on. Some of the habitat management was a little over-enthusiastic and some vegetation clearance continued into the water itself. Water voles are not going to sit out in the open while strimming takes place so they may leave the area and may or may not return.

---

7) There were just three sightings of water voles — all reported by the author.

OPPOSITE PAGE: Scenes along the Cromford Canal, including the barge, which operates in high season between Cromford Wharf and High Peak Junction.

'High Peak Junction was probably our best spot until about 2010. Last year we hardly saw any water voles for the last five months. Often they weren't very visible even though there were a few signs. It's disastrous, absolutely disastrous. The decline is not only in activity signs but also visual sightings by people that walk the canal every day. They are still there but there are so few so you just don't see them. There are very few activity signs such as latrines and feeding remains so it's difficult to tell how many water voles there might be. This year we haven't had any recent signs of mink and the rafts are checked regularly, so mink don't appear to be affecting the voles. However, from Cromford Wharf to High Peak Junction the water levels have been kept higher to accommodate the barge. Ledges where water voles used to sit and where they left their latrines can't be seen anymore.

'Everything that's done on the Cromford Canal is planned around people and wildlife. It's got to be detailed and structured. In one respect there is a benefit because of the volume of people who can enjoy this special place. It is difficult for the council. They've got this balance between people and wildlife and it doesn't always agree and it's very difficult to manage.'
SHIRLEY FREEMAN

Helen Perkins who organised the county survey and co-wrote *The Water Vole in Derbyshire* (1999) now works for the national body, The Wildlife Trust. She believes that the Cromford Canal population was always vulnerable:

'It is possible that the Cromford Canal population persisted longer than those on the nearby River Derwent because of human presence acting as a deterrent to mink colonisation. Unfortunately, the isolation of this population over several years may have made its extinction inevitable. The loss of this much-loved population provides a salutary warning of just how vulnerable Derbyshire's remaining water vole populations remain.'
HELEN PERKINS

OPPOSITE PAGE: Water vole at High Peak Junction eating broad-leaved pondweed, which dominates this section of the Cromford Canal. Some feeding platforms like this have been submerged under the higher water levels needed to accommodate the barge.

BENTLEY BROOK AND LUMSDALE

Bentley Brook rises on Matlock Moor and flows south through Cuckoostone Dale then into Lumsdale where the stream falls with such force from a great height that it has carved a series of waterfalls through the limestone. The Lumsdale gorge is one of the most spectacular of all the waterways of Derbyshire and Lumsdale is, according to the Arkwright Society, 'one of the best examples of a water-powered industrial archaeological site in Great Britain and it is unusual to see such extensive use of water power in such a relatively small area'. Rocky streams and waterfalls are the last place to find water voles but they have made their way along this watercourse in the past. They were found in the 1997–1999 survey both above Lumsdale and on the lower part of Bentley Brook close to where it meets the Derwent at Matlock Green.

RIVER DERWENT FROM MATLOCK TO BAMFORD

The main River Derwent has traditionally been occupied by water voles but little survey work along the river has taken place over the last 20 years. There are many stretches of the Derwent that support good habitat for water voles. The flow of the river is slowed along some stretches by its meander through pastoral land and there are steep banks covered with lush vegetation. The Derwent's banks are pockmarked with stretches of burrow entrances running for considerable distances, interrupted only by shaded stretches or places where the current runs too fast. The truth is, the main River Derwent is not sufficiently well surveyed for us to know how well populated it is. My own survey sites are north of Matlock town centre, and in numerous searches of the riverbank I have seen just one water vole on the Derwent between Matlock and Rowsley, indicating that the long runs of burrows evident on this stretch must have been deserted long ago.

The picture is less bleak going north, with numerous sightings of water voles between Chatsworth and Froggatt. Where trees line the banks of the Derwent, riparian plant growth is inhibited making these stretches untenable for water voles. There is considerable damage to the riverbank where cattle have trampled both to drink and graze. Sheep graze along many miles of fields that surround the river, and there is no fencing to keep them away from the banks that are potentially home to the water vole. Unlike cattle, they are able to negotiate the steep riverbanks and in doing so they compact the earth and strip out much of the vegetation as it is emerging in the spring, where it would provide vital cover for water voles that are most active at this time finding new territory and seeking mates.

OPPOSITE PAGE, LEFT: Sheep grazing above the banks of the Derwent in Chatsworth park while a water vole grazes below at the water line in the bottom right of the picture. RIGHT: The spectacular waterfall at Lumsdale.

Spring on the Derwent: the view south across the weir at Froggatt with Curbar and Baslow edges on the skyline.

Late summer on the Derwent, below Froggatt.

Autumn on the Derwent, looking downstream from below Northwood, Darley Dale.

Winter on the Derwent, looking upstream from below Northwood, Darley Dale. Much of the Derwent is fringed with trees, which inhibits the growth of waterside vegetation making its shaded banks unsuitable for water voles.

PONDS

There are between 2,000 and 3,000 ponds in the Peak District, three quarters of which are in the White Peak. Many of these ponds are 19th-century dewponds used before the days of groundwater abstraction as a vital water source for stock in the dry limestone pastures. There are also village ponds, farm ponds, millponds, fish ponds and those associated with mining and quarrying. In parts of the Peak District half of the ponds were lost during the 1970s and 1980s by leakage, damage from stock or they were polluted by sheep-dip, herbicides, slurry or silage run-off.

Ponds are part of a linked patchwork of water habitat both in the countryside and in urban gardens and parks. They are home to such rare species as the great crested newt and other amphibians, numerous invertebrate species and also the water vole. I have heard accounts of water voles living in garden ponds and watched them in various millponds and fish ponds in the White Peak and in a pond in the Whitworth park in Darley Dale.

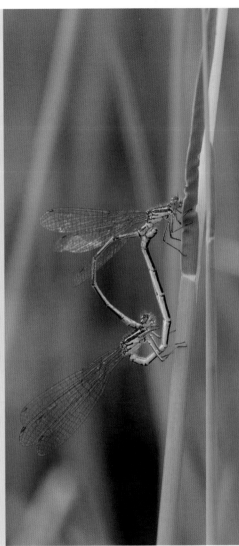

TOP LEFT: Grassmoor pond, north-east Derbyshire. BOTTOM LEFT: Pond in Whitworth park, Darley Dale.
RIGHT: Azure damselflies mating and laying eggs.

The Wye at Water-cum-Jolly Dale.

WHITE PEAK RIVERS

There are many dry valleys in the White Peak, and rivers that flow underground in drier seasons. The high plateau of the White Peak extends from Castleton in the north to Matlock and Wirksworth in the south. It is cut through with steep-sided gorges, the largest of which are the dales of the Dove and the Wye. These limestone rivers run year-round, but the rivers Lathkill and Bradford often have low flows, with some sections drying out altogether as the watercourses flow underground in periods of low rainfall. The subterranean world of the White Peak, with its immense caverns, tunnels, cave systems, sinkholes and underground rivers, has been altered by many centuries of lead mining and sough driving. As a consequence, the hydrology of the area is complex and ever-changing with blockages, flooding,

and uncertain flows. For many people, the limestone rivers and streams and their millponds and fish ponds represent the classic habitat for water voles. Many rivers and streams in the White Peak are still occupied by water voles, but during periods of low flow the voles can be left high and dry.

RIVER WYE

The Wye has traditionally been regarded as a stronghold for the water vole. The river rises at Combs Moss above Buxton and flows through the town before its descent, along a straightened and canalised course, beside the A6 through Ashwood Dale. The tree cover and intense modification of the river make the first two-mile stretch south of Buxton unsuitable for water voles. The Wye then winds its way through some of the Peak District's most spectacular limestone dales. Wyedale, Chee Dale, Miller's Dale, Water-cum-Jolly Dale and Monsal Dale are deep, rocky gorges popular with hikers, climbers and dog walkers. Disturbance to wildlife is a considerable issue here, as elsewhere in the Peak District National Park.

The tight meanders of the River Wye have created varied flows of fast, shallow water running over gravels and deeper channels of slow-running water. Along many stretches of the Wye where the current is slow and the bank profile suitable there are runs of water vole burrows.

The Wye's course from Chee Dale to Bakewell has open stretches of deep water in several millponds and associated mill leats that are familiar haunts for water voles. While parts of the dales are dark with shadowed areas and tree cover, there are many open areas with wide swathes of lush vegetation and grassy banksides. With its pure water and varied habitat, much of the Wye from Wye Dale to Bakewell and beyond is perfect territory for water voles. Once commonly seen in Bakewell on the riverbanks through Scott's Meadow, on mill leats or close to riverside paths near the town centre, water voles have now become scarce or absent from many sites in the town.

The last stretch of the Wye seems to hold out the best hope for water voles. There are much quieter areas and no public access through the flood plain meadows near the confluence with the Derwent at Rowsley and through here the Haddon Estate's river keeper monitors mink continuously.

Water vole burrow entrances are much in evidence along the Wye.

OPPOSITE PAGE, TOP LEFT: Water vole, well concealed by reeds. BOTTOM LEFT: The Wye at Scott's Meadow, Bakewell.
OPPOSITE PAGE, RIGHT: Water-cum-Jolly Dale.

RIVER LATHKILL

'Lathkin is, by many degrees, the purest and most transparent stream that I ever saw, either at home or abroad; and breeds, 'tis said, the reddest and the best Trouts in England.' (Charles Cotton in *The Compleat Angler*, Part II.)

The River Lathkill rises below Monyash in the stony upper reaches of Lathkill Dale. The river ceases to flow over much of its length through drier seasons and while dams retain some water, water voles that spread up the valley can become isolated when the rest of the river disappears.[8]

When the water table is high, water gushes from Lathkill Head Cave but it is more usually fed by springs lower down the valley. The weirs at the lower end of the Lathkill retain water all year round and water voles have been seen there, and also beyond Conksbury Bridge on the last section of the river that flows through water meadows before joining the River Bradford at Alport. The loss of flow on both the Lathkill and the Bradford is mainly due to leakage caused by centuries of lead mining. There are plans to stop up some of the leaks in the Lathkill in order to restore year-round flow, which may make this valley a more reliable home for the water vole in future.

---

8) Having been told of water voles in one of the dams in Lathkill Dale in August 2014, I went to check in September and walked almost two miles along the dale from below Over Haddon before I could find any water and, unsurprisingly, no sign of water voles.

TOP: The Lathkill at Alport. BOTTOM: The isolated shallow waters of the River Lathkill in Lathkill Dale in summer. The Lathkill dries out along much of its length most years.

RIVER BRADFORD

The River Bradford runs for just four miles from where it rises in Gratton Dale to its confluence with the Lathkill at Alport. Water voles have been recorded, both in the past and recently, along most of the watercourse that has public access.

The river runs through a series of three limestone dales – Gratton Dale, Fishpond (or Rollow Dale) then through a wide-open floodplain meadow before it enters the deep gorge of Bradford Dale. Here the valley floor is dominated by six dams which were built in the 19th century both for industry and trout fishing. Much of the river's course is heavily modified with straightened and canalised stretches and extensive areas of open water.

The upper reaches of the river provide ideal habitat for water voles as they are secluded and surrounded by rich vegetation, but browsing cattle have broken down banks and burrows and destroyed many stands of marginal vegetation that have sustained small colonies of water voles in the past. Fluctuating water levels have made most of the dammed sections of the river unusable. Where stock graze in an open area of grassland below Youlgrave, the flow of the stream is shallow and braided and there is no bankside structure to allow water voles to burrow.

In the last section of the river the stream flows along a deep and narrow channel that has provided the best habitat for water voles. But here, as elsewhere along this popular stream, the constant traffic of people and dogs causes considerable disturbance to small populations that continue to occupy this stretch.

TOP: The River Bradford fenced off to protect the wall (used by water voles) and to provide a wide margin of vegetation where previously cattle had broken down burrows by browsing along the stream margins. BOTTOM: The River Bradford in the popular Brookleton where the flow is often shallow and there is no bankside structure.

Loss of flow during dry summers has meant the desertion or extinction of colonies, and severe flooding such as that in June 2007 washed away a colony of water voles that had returned to the upper reaches of the Bradford after many years of absence. The river keeper for the Haddon Estate monitors for mink, and a refuge area for water voles has been created with funding secured by a local group: the Bradford River Action Group working with the co-operation of local farmers and the Haddon Estate. The pure waters and rich plant life on this limestone stream make it ideal for water voles, but as with other Peak District rivers there are issues over the conflicting interests of people and wildlife. The simple act of fencing out stock and dogs has transformed this habitat.

TOP LEFT: The River Bradford late summer where marginal plants have been grazed by cattle and sheep. **TOP RIGHT:** Fences erected in early spring to protect the bank profile and allow the riparian margin to recover. **BOTTOM LEFT:** River Bradford near Alport. **BOTTOM RIGHT:** Early in the first summer (2015) after the margins of the river had been fenced off.

RIVER NOE AND BRADWELL BROOK

The River Noe flows through Edale then into the Hope Valley to join the Derwent at Bamford. Despite the excellent water quality, evidence of past occupation and suitable habitat along parts of the Noe, there are no recent records of water voles on the river. Various streams in the upper Hope Valley including Peakshole Water, farm ditches, ponds and the pools at Hope cement works were inhabited by water voles from 1997–1999 according to the Derbyshire Wildlife Trust survey.

Bradwell Brook is a limestone stream that rises in the centre of Bradwell. With its wide swathes of layered waterside vegetation, it has long been regarded as a stronghold for the water vole. The stream is rich in biodiversity, bordered by wet woodland and unimproved grassland along much of its one and a half miles from Bradwell to the confluence with the River Noe at Brough. There are still colonies of water voles on the brook on

private land so it is to be hoped that mink can be controlled there in the future. The survey of 1997–1999 had found mink scats and no water voles, which makes the return of the water vole there a few years later a great cause for celebration. In 2007 a remarkable film, *The Water Voles of Bradwell Brook*, was made by Paul Nicols and featured several vole dramas including territorial fights, an adult driving off her weaned young and a stoat stalking a water vole, together with many other vignettes of wildlife on this beautiful stream. The film also showed the devastating effects of the summer storms in 2007, which caused serious flooding across much of Derbyshire and South Yorkshire and disrupted or destroyed water vole colonies on many occupied sites.

TOP: River Noe. BOTTOM: Bradwell Brook.

WATER FOR PEOPLE

The Derwent is a highly modified river that has been dammed, canalised and diverted over centuries of use for running mills and supplying water. Just a few miles from its source, it flows into three extensive reservoirs: Howden, Derwent and Ladybower. The valleys of the upper Derwent were flooded and the villages of Ashopton and Derwent were lost in the first half of the 20th century to supply Sheffield, Nottingham and Leicester with water. Water is also taken from the River Noe and the River Ashop to supply the reservoir system. Much further south, the upper reaches of the River Amber are dammed at Ogston reservoir.

The Derwent reservoirs were built at a time when there was no attempt to accommodate wildlife, unlike the more recently constructed and sensitively managed Carsington Water that has reedbeds, ponds, scrapes for waders, varied bank profiles and gently sloping shorelines. Around the feeder streams of the Derwent reservoirs there are beds of *Juncus effusus* (soft rush) that are potential habitat for water voles, but on the whole, these vast bodies of water alternate between being full to the brim or (when levels drop) exposing huge areas of steeply sloping concrete that cannot be used by water voles.

Ladybower reservoir seen from Derwent Edge.

UPPER DERWENT

The Derbyshire Wildlife Trust survey of 1997–1999 found evidence of water vole occupation just below Swains Greave at 490 metres where the Derwent rises and in the upper part of the River Westend at 570 metres. They were also found in several moorland streams on both Strines and Moscar Moor and in Ladybower Brook.

The lower stretches of the rivers Ashop and Alport had been occupied by water voles until 1993. These populations disappeared as cattle destroyed a large area of *Juncus* in Alport Dale and water levels dropped in the River Ashop due to abstraction. High up on Alport Moor a survey of the headstreams of the River Ashop in 2003 showed extensive evidence of water vole presence and breeding signs. Searching in these remote areas is challenging and my own exploration of the remote Alport valley revealed no signs.

The streams that run below Stanage Edge and upper Burbage Brook have thriving colonies of water voles. Recently the gating of the Long Causeway track over Stanage to exclude off-road vehicles has allowed the habitat to recover and water voles have returned to streams that had been churned up and disturbed by traffic.

ABOVE: River Alport in the upper Alport valley: the steep fall and rocky streambed make this unsuitable for water voles. Water voles have been recorded in the past higher up in the more level catchment streams and lower down in the river's flood plain. RIGHT: Upland streams on the North Lees estate below Stanage Edge have strong water vole populations.

EASTERN MOORS

The Eastern Moors support populations of water voles in tiny connecting streams and ditches. Bar Brook runs for three miles through Big Moor and supports thriving populations of water voles along its tightly meandering course.

Leash Fen is linked to this stream and while it is almost impossible to survey, this large expanse of secluded, marshy fenland could be densely occupied by water voles. Other streams, conduits and drainage ditches on the Eastern Moors are home to the water vole but frequent extinctions and recolonisations in this territory probably occur without anyone knowing.

ABOVE: Bar Brook on Big Moor. OPPOSITE PAGE, TOP LEFT: Cattle graze along Bar Brook on Big Moor. TOP RIGHT: 18th-century stone bridge across Bar Brook. BOTTOM LEFT: East Moor clad in heather in August. BOTTOM RIGHT: Black Leach Brook on Leash Fen.

Water voles in uplands

The high, exposed territory of the Dark Peak moors with its boggy ground, pools and tiny headstreams now supports regionally important populations of water voles. Most people associate the water vole with gently flowing lowland streams and with rivers fringed with lush vegetation but much of this kind of territory has been lost through development, over-grazing or disturbance. Most crucially, the expansion of mink through all our major river systems has caused many water vole extinctions along our lowland rivers. It is tempting to think that facing the perils of mink in the river valleys and lowlands, water voles took to the hills to escape and find refuge. But it is more likely that they were always there and that no one had thought to look for them until quite recently. The extent to which upland watercourses are occupied by water voles has only been understood over the last 30 years or so.

The high moorland of the Dark Peak can appear positively hostile with vast swathes of impenetrable heather, blanket bog, cotton grass and coarse sedges intersected by deep ditches and streams that are narrow, often undercut and almost concealed from view. It is surprising to find that water voles live in this often wind-blasted territory, their burrows tucked into the dark banks of peat hags and with runways forming little tunnels through tussock grass. But colonies of water voles living in uplands are now regarded as one of the most important targets for conservation action as they have persisted while many lowland populations have been devastated.

River Alport. Once occupied by water voles, now the banks are badly eroded and the voles have gone.

The importance of upland habitats as refuge for water voles has made this kind of territory the subject of intensive research in Scotland, Wales, the Peak District and northern England. Small colonies in upland areas and grouped within a broad regional location are described by scientists as a 'metapopulation'. Together these small groups of animals form important functioning populations that are able to disperse, link up and recolonise even though there may be a high level of extinctions. There has been considerable research into the ways in which upland colonies of water voles function. One piece of research in Scotland used DNA sequencing to determine the parentage of individual water voles and dispersal distance from natal territory (i.e. where the voles were born) in order to assess how robust small fragmented populations are in terms of genetic diversity.[9] Other research has looked into habitat preference, population density, territorial behaviour, dispersal and other behaviours that influence how well a group of linked populations or 'metapopulation' can function in isolated upland habitats.

9) Telfer, Piertney, Dallas, Stewart, Marshall, Gow and Lambin, 'Parentage assignment detects frequent and large-scale dispersal in water voles' in *Molecular Ecology*, Vol.12, No.7 (2003).

Some small, isolated colonies of water voles in upland areas may just be composed of a single pair of monogamous adults. It is thought that the risk of inbreeding increases the drive to disperse far and wide. Dispersal distances covered by juveniles and young adult water voles in this kind of terrain can be considerable. The average dispersal distances covered by females in highly fragmented upland populations studied in Scotland was 1.9 to 2.45 kilometres, and 1.4 to 1.9 kilometres in males. Animals were found to travel both overground and along watercourses.

Water voles have been found living above 900 metres in Scotland, so altitude has not halted their spread into apparently harsh environments. However upland streams that flow fast down steep gradients over stony ground cannot be used by water voles. They favour slow-flowing water, dense, lush vegetation and soft banks in which to burrow. They can also live in extensive beds of *Juncus effusus* where they are known to construct nests above ground which are – apparently – the size of a football. This may be a response to the dangers of flooding which is a constant threat to upland water voles and such nests provide a place to evade predators.

Water voles feed happily on the limited range of plants available on moorland, especially rush, grass and sedge species as well as waterweeds. They will also eat flowers such as tormentil and heath bedstraw. In the autumn little piles of white pith from rushes may be found, where water voles have stripped off the outer

TOP: A stream on the North Lees estate with a water vole latrine in the foreground and Stanage Edge on the skyline. BOTTOM: Water vole latrine on an upland stream.

green layer for their winter food stores. Field voles also leave such piles, and may leave droppings close by which help to identify the feeding signs as being from another vole species.

Water voles are very difficult to see in upland habitats as vegetation can obstruct any sight of tiny streams, and dense beds of *Juncus* conceal their activities very effectively. Their behaviour is different from their lowland counterparts; they are more secretive in their habits and apt to disappear fast when startled as they are unused to any sight, sound or scent of humans. This territory is extremely difficult to survey as the world of the water vole is well concealed by almost impenetrable vegetation. The locations are often remote, the ground is difficult and in many places it is hard to view the watercourse and to penetrate surrounding vegetation to search for signs of occupation. Because of this, most of upland Britain has never been surveyed.[10] However, it can be astonishing to find evidence of intense water vole activity with latrines, feeding signs, scattered droppings and numerous burrow entrances in a kind of underworld of dark amber water, punctuated by rocks or shingle beaches amid tight, winding corridors with blackened walls of peaty soil.

10) I have spent five days searching five kilometres (3 miles) of an upland stream and saw many signs of occupation and not one water vole.

LEFT: A tiny stream winding through a spinney on the North Lees estate, seen from water vole level.

THREATS TO UPLAND WATER VOLES
MINK

Upland populations of water voles are fragmented and vulnerable to predation by both aerial and terrestrial predators. Foxes, stoats and weasels live on the moors, and the skies are patrolled by kestrels, buzzards, goshawks and owls.

While mink have been found on upland watercourses, the lack of trees makes it harder for them to find their most favoured den sites in open moorland and the variety and abundance of prey species is limited. However when mink do get into this territory, they can cause devastation to tiny and naturally fragmented populations of water voles.

GRAZING

While the number of sheep grazing in uplands has been much reduced in the last 20 years, where sheep congregate to ford a stream or to drink, they continue to have a detrimental effect on upland watercourses and surrounding vegetation. There are conservation measures and agri-environment schemes aimed at improving upland habitat for waders and other wildlife with measures to restrict stocking levels in sensitive areas. But recent changes to stewardship agreements appear to offer far less cash incentives to upland farmers.

There tend to be low densities of cattle in uplands but they can still cause considerable damage to banks and burrow systems, particularly as upland breeds tend to browse on emergent plants and use the streams as a source of drinking water. On Big Moor there is a large population of red deer that make use of many crossing and drinking places on Bar Brook, thus destroying stretches of potential water vole habitat.

WATERCOURSE MAINTENANCE

Drainage conduits and ditches with slow-flowing water can provide ideal habitat for water voles and if they are stone-lined, voles will use often use the walls as burrow entrances. Ditch and reservoir maintenance work can cause damage to water vole burrows when mechanical diggers are used to clear silt out of channels or when vegetation is cleared leaving banks exposed.

TOP: Female kestrel. MIDDLE: Long-eared owl with field vole.
BOTTOM: A sheep surveys the damage done to a stream bank by her and others.

122

DROUGHT AND FLOOD

Weather conditions dictate how suitable territory is for water voles. Dry weather can dry out marshy areas and alter how streams flow, which can be a positive change in some fast-flowing streams. But drought can also make some habitat unusable. Extreme heavy rainfall can be devastating and close monitoring by Derbyshire Wildlife Trust of sample water vole sites in the Peak District moors between 1999 and 2003 revealed the impact of different extremes of weather:

'In July 2002 a one hundred year rainfall event obliterated approximately 80% of the water vole habitat at this site. During such events a rapid rise in water levels may flood burrows and the movement of significant amounts of rock material downstream may cause the death of some water voles. The trend towards wetter winters and a greater frequency of floods may threaten colonies and impact on the viability of neighbouring populations. At sites susceptible to damage by heavy rainfall or drought conditions, the potential for creating refuge areas, for example off-line ponds and marshy areas, should be considered.'[11]

The impact of extreme weather and particular conservation issues concerning water voles in uplands is explored further in Part 7.

---

11) Derbyshire Wildlife Trust and National Trust, *Water Voles in the Uplands* (Belper, 2004).

TOP AND MIDDLE: The River Bradford where the stream has burst its banks in a stretch usually occupied by water voles.
BOTTOM: The River Lathkill flooded near Alport. Low-lying streams are slower to flood than the upland catchment streams but floods that occur anywhere can devastate water vole populations.

Disturbance

CATTLE

Much of lowland Derbyshire and the White Peak is pastoral cattle country. Floodplain pastures have been used for grazing dairy and beef herds for centuries, and rivers and streams have traditionally provided animals with a source of drinking water. The emergent and semi-emergent plants growing along the margins of our watercourses, lakes and ponds are nutrient rich and cattle make a beeline for them. In doing so, they effectively remove swathes of vegetation that are both food and valuable habitat for the water vole.

There is evidence of cattle causing erosion by breaking down (often called 'poaching') river and stream banks throughout Derbyshire in lowland and upland areas, and especially along the limestone streams and rivers of the Derbyshire Dales. When cattle wander through burrows occupied by water voles, the networks of tunnels and chambers are instantly destroyed. When banks are broken down, the steeply sloping bank profile which water voles need is lost and ground gets compacted. It becomes impossible for water voles to recolonise areas once they are wrecked by browsing cattle.

Where cattle ford streams and rivers or go to drink, they will often enter and make their way along the watercourse snatching at vegetation as they go and damaging the structure of the riparian margin. They also disturb the riverbed and churn up clouds of suspended solids which affect water quality and habitat downstream. In addition to all this, cattle defecate into the water altering the biological balance of the watercourse and its ecology, increasing nutrients that cause certain plants to flourish while others are suppressed. Changes in nutrient

River Wye near Ashford in the Water, once occupied by water voles and now showing damage by cattle in the foreground.

levels can cause algal blooms which can destroy sensitive ecosystems killing insects and fish and causing an overall loss of biodiversity.

Quite often the simple solution to these problems is fencing to prevent stock from entering areas occupied by water voles, or any other environmentally sensitive parts of a watercourse. This buffer fencing can also bring benefits for water quality by protecting the river from pollution and run-off from soils.

OPPOSITE PAGE: A cow drinks at a badly eroded bankside on the Derwent.

However, these buffer strips usually require some grazing or management so that the open and lush habitats preferred by water voles can be sustained. Farmers, quite understandably, do not wish to lose valuable areas of grazing or access to water for their stock. In recognition of this, agri-environment schemes – such as the new Countryside Stewardship scheme, which opened in 2015 – enable farmers to apply for funding to undertake measures that protect priority rivers.[12]

Warren Slaney is head river keeper for the Haddon Estate and manages 27 miles of river on the Derwent, the Wye, the Lathkill and the Bradford. He showed me two contrasting ways of managing farmland adjacent to the River Derwent and he was quite open in his opinion of one tenant farmer:

'This farmer has shown himself to be incapable of looking after the land in the long term properly. It's to do with the dairy-farming ethos. They just look at grass as money, just grass, that's all they want, just grass. They don't want herbs as they get all their minerals from licks. Everywhere you look on a dairy farm there's just compacted land and grass and wet poo. Dairy farmers think of the land as grass and money. This is not healthy ground. All the ground is compacted and there's nothing but thistles so they have to keep spraying all the time. They don't let the hedgerows grow up into berries; it's all trimmed and shorn. It's like a milking parlour – there's nothing to it. There's no room for wildlife on a dairy farm. It's all about grass and money and misery – you never see a happy dairy farmer. Farmers who own land should have a completely different attitude to life on the farm because they are building the future. "Live like you're going to die tomorrow, farm like you're going to live forever."'

As milk prices have once again been driven well below the cost of production by supermarket pricing, small operators are giving up at the rate of nearly two every day. It is no wonder that wildlife conservation comes low on the agenda for most dairy farmers. Patrick Holden, himself an organic dairy farmer writing in *The Observer* in August 2015, blames the government, the National Farmers' Union and most large food retailers for allowing food and farming to be at the mercy of global trade, fluctuating market prices and cycles of boom and bust and for the failure 'to put an economic value on the damaging impact of intensive farming'.

'The enlargement of average farm size, the abandonment of mixed farming in favour of continuous commodity production using chemical fertilisers and pesticides, the reduction of the agricultural workforce … may have increased yields and lowered food prices, but at enormous cost, in terms of lost soil fertility, biodiversity, jobs, skills, social and cultural capital and diminished food security and negative impact on public health. Incredibly, none of these losses has been priced, as a result of which we are living in a world of dishonest food pricing,

---

12) Details of the new Countryside Stewardship scheme can be found on the government's website: <https://www.gov.uk/government/publications/countryside-stewardship-manual-print-version> Natural England, the Peak District National Park Authority or Derbyshire Wildlife Trust has more info.

where the polluter doesn't pay and, conversely, the farmers who are delivering public and environmental benefits are not rewarded financially for so doing.'

'If our small farms are allowed to wither, the whole nation will suffer.'[13]

Many small family dairy farmers across Derbyshire have given up dairy farming or switched to beef. Many of those that remain now work with larger herds often on more intensively managed land. The switch to silage and the loss of species-rich hay meadows and other traditional pastures over the last 40 years has turned many parts of the Peak District into a wildlife desert.

My own exploration of miles of Derbyshire's riverbanks has given me a clear picture of the extent of the problem of erosion caused by cattle even on land that is managed sensitively. Warren believes that the solution lies in separating watercourses from agriculture altogether and giving farmers an incentive to do so:

'The only way to get a fence back on land that you don't own is for Natural England or the Peak Park to say any land that's put into buffer stripping will attract a higher rate of grant or subsidy. So the farmers think, "it makes sense for me to do that". You need a carrot and stick. We're all in a difficult position because the farming lobby is very powerful. They generally get what they want and nobody wants to say anything. Look at the dredging that took place in the south-west. It was rubbish, it was pointless, but they did it anyway.'

Warren showed me an extensive stretch of the Derwent that the Haddon Estate has taken back into direct management in order to keep both the land and the river and its margins healthy. The unstable and eroded banks were being worn away by high winter flows.

'When we took over it was infested by Himalayan balsam, which is another problem because when the winter comes it dies back and it's out-competed all the native plants. So there's nothing but bare soil, which compounds the problem. So it was land use, it was cattle grazing the grass off the top

The Derwent's banks near Darley Dale show the natural recovery of bankside vegetation that has secured this fast flowing section of the river from bank erosion caused by winter flood levels.

13) Holden, 'If our small farms are allowed to wither, the whole nation will suffer' in *The Observer* (9 August 2015) [website] <http://www.theguardian.com/commentisfree/2015/aug/09/lose-small-farms-britains-heritage-gone>

of the bank and balsam out-competing native plants. We took over management of that land. We managed to get about 15 metres of buffer strip on top of the bank, not to the river margin. There would be about 25 metres altogether. We've got a full, wide margin of protection now between agriculture and the river. This is extensive organic agriculture – the very best kind but it's still harmful to the river. Once people take a crop of the hay or silage they are often asked or instructed by the stewardship requirement to graze and the cattle go straight back into the river to graze the lush mineral-rich marginal verge. The river would be in sensible proportions with grazing deer which are low-impact, not huge great dairy cows with their massive feet that scramble up and down the bank and break it off.

'As soon as we fence out agriculture, immediately you start to get grass dying back leaving little tents and you get field voles in there immediately. There are almost no field voles in the field but they are in the buffer strip. You can identify where the buffer strips are by where the kestrels are. All these buffer zones add up to more and more land that's in protection, that's fenced off from agriculture.

'It's sad that we can't look after land properly and have rivers that tourists can enjoy and not have fences. It's sad that we can't have rivers and agriculture alongside each other, but there are 64 million people in this country that need feeding and it's not possible. So the buffer stripping is critical to what we're doing here; improving water quality and restoring rivers. But it's hard work. You fence off the riverbank and immediately you're responsible for the weed-control. You don't make any friends at all if you've got a strip of land with seeding ragwort everywhere or thistles. So you've got to be aware when you do that, you've got to get the strimmer out, not weedkiller but the strimmer. You make sure everything's strimmed at the right time of year and the ragwort's pulled.

'The payoff is that when it's right, in no time at all you get sweet rocket, hemp-agrimony, willow herb, meadowsweet, and campion – proper riverside plants. The diversity that comes on a riverside is astonishing. You get the semi-emergent plants, the watercresses and the speedwells and you get the fully emerged riverside plants that grow on the banks and bind it together. And that's the ideal habitat for the water voles, because they've got the cover from the aerial predation and they just feel safe. All animals feel safe with cover over their heads.'

OPPOSITE PAGE TOP LEFT: Fallow deer by the Derwent in Chatsworth. BOTTOM LEFT: Erosion caused by cattle and sheep on the banks of the Derwent at Rowsley. RIGHT: 'All animals feel safe with cover over their heads.'

DISTURBANCE BY PEOPLE AND DOGS

In land-locked Derbyshire, watery places are a magnet to both visitors and residents. On a warm summer's day many people beat a path to the nearest river, stream, lake or reservoir. The squeals of excited children, cacophony of dogs barking, loud voices and laughter are the joyous sounds of people having a good time. But such disturbance often has unfortunate consequences for the wild creatures that live in these places. The diurnal habits of water voles frequently bring them into direct contact with the activities of people. The water voles' breeding season from April to September is also the busiest period of human activity in the Peak District and other tourist hotspots in Derbyshire. Water voles must deal with disturbance by retreat – making the most of the increasingly limited periods of peace and quiet to feed and move around their territory. While water voles have generally been regarded as easy to watch at close quarters, any sudden noise or intrusion will send them into the water, or burrow, or under cover. Where there is almost constant traffic of people and dogs, the pressure can make the habitat untenable. On the rivers where a right of way runs along one bank it is noticeable that most burrow systems are along the opposite bank, but if the bank profile closest to a footpath is most suitable then water voles are forced into close proximity with dogs and people. Along narrow waterways water voles will make use of burrows on both banks.

Layers of dense waterside vegetation provide water voles with the best protection from disturbance but this does not develop until early to mid summer and it is in the springtime that over-wintering water voles are establishing breeding territories or searching for new territory. So they are forced into the open along busy waterways during the most critical period for the development of breeding colonies. If they are disturbed too much they will simply move on and may be forced to settle in less than optimal habitat with fewer chances of establishing breeding colonies.

DOGS IN THE WATER

The fragile world of the small mammal is fraught with perils and threats unseen by us. Much of this world is beyond the consciousness and sense of humans but it is right on the canine radar. A dog's world is made up of scent trails and their unerring instincts take them into the heart of the unprotected worlds of prey animals – like that of our most threatened and endangered mammal, the water vole.

According to the Pet Food Manufacturing Association there were 9 million dogs in the UK in 2014, which means that nearly a quarter of all British households have one. Dogs need emptying at least twice daily and so, in time-honoured fashion, the dog walk often takes place along a riverbank or canal towpath. Part of the fun of this is that the dog gets to jump in the water, clean itself up a bit and have a chance to chase things. Dogs are able to search out and kill water voles but as they rarely manage to catch either waterfowl or water voles, many dog owners regard their activity in or near the water as harmless. They are not aware that their dog's gleeful splashing and barking may be one of very many canine intrusions into the water that could cause a population of water voles to collapse under pressure.

I was in a country park photographing a water vole that vanished as a terrier appeared and sniffed its way along the grassy tunnels and holes at the margin of an old mining flash pond. His owner came into view and asked, 'did he disturb something – what was it?'
'A water vole,' I replied.
'Oh, that's his favourite.'

This encounter is typical of many I have had while researching this book.

part5

The History of the Water
Vole in Britain

The history of the water vole in Britain

The water vole was here when Britain was connected to Continental Europe by land bridges across the Channel and the North Sea 9,000 years ago. This gives the water vole its status as a true native of Britain, but its presence goes back much further. Early ancestors of the water vole lived in Britain over 2.5 million years ago – a period when a much warmer Earth was beginning to cool at the onset of the first Ice Age.

Derbyshire has an extensive fossil record of mammals that once roamed the county, preserved in beds of rock and sediments in the limestone. Notable finds such as the bones of the 'Allenton hippopotamus' were unearthed close to Derby in the 19th century, where it probably swam with the water voles in the River Derwent around 120,000 years ago (during the Ipswichian interglacial). Some of the earliest British fossil fauna records from the early Pleistocene were found in a cave in Dove Holes near Buxton. Rare finds here included a sabre-toothed cat. Incredibly this site was quarried to become a municipal rubbish dump. However the most substantial finds from this period were in marine clays in East Anglia. There, among many other mammals, were several forbears of the water vole together with mastodon, elephant, tapir, three-toed horse, rhinoceros, panda and hyena.[1]

The Pleistocene dates from the first signs of the Earth cooling around 2.5 million years ago. This period spanned great cycles of climate change characterised by ice ages or 'glacials' when much of the land was covered by ice, interspersed by warmer intervals when the glaciers retreated, called interglacials. When the glaciers retreated, areas became habitable and mammals including early species of humans, migrated on to the land mass that is now Britain. Periods of cooling drove mammals away from the encroaching ice, and when ice covered much of the northern hemisphere many species of animals became extinct, or were forced to migrate to isolated pockets that were free of ice. Where populations became established in more hospitable environments, they were able to secure a base from which they could later disperse.[2]

The current distribution of species in the northern hemisphere originates from the gradual northwards migration of populations as ice retreated after the last glaciation. Today's native British mammal fauna has its origins at the end of the Pleistocene epoch, around 12,000 years ago.

---

1) Yalden, *The History of British Mammals* (London, 1999), p14.   2) In Britain there were three named glaciations, the Anglian, Wolstonian and Devensian, and the interglacials which are named the Cromerian (a warmer period before the onset of the Anglian glacial), Hoxnian, Ipswichian and Flandrian (the latter of which we are now in). Study of deep-sea temperature records shows a more complex picture of many more cycles of cooling and warming.

OPPOSITE PAGE: Autumn mist in the Derwent valley, viewed from Big Moor.

The first water voles

The History of British Mammals by Derek Yalden (1999) **provides a comprehensive picture of the history and evolution of all species of mammals that have lived in Britain with a considerable focus on the mammals of Derbyshire. This essential work is the basis of much of the following account.**

In East Anglia the Cromer forest bed consists of deposits of sands, gravels and mud that date from 500,000 to 2.5 million years ago. Thousands of fossilised mammals have been found in the layers exposed in the eroding cliffs and foreshore around the coast of Norfolk and Suffolk, which are of global importance. The very earliest species of water vole were among the earliest mammals found, and finds from later interglacials confirm that they persisted as a species evolving over many thousands of years.

The water vole's ancestor *Mimomys savini* was the most common mammal found in the rock and clay layers along the coast at West Runton in Norfolk.

This early species of water vole differed from the later *Arvicola cantiana*, found at Ostend on the Norfolk coast and dated as the late Cromerian. *Mimomys savini* had molar teeth that were rooted whereas *A. cantiana* evolved with unrooted teeth that continued to grow through its life and which were better adapted to the tougher plant material associated with a colder climate (such as reeds and sedges).[3]

The water vole appears as a common species in both of its earlier forms so that the presence of one or the other species in bone assemblages has helped scientists to date the interglacials that these findings represent. As the later water vole evolved over thousands of years, its fossil records reveal transitional phases between *A. cantiana* and *A. terrestris/A. amphibius* (the present-day water vole).

The water vole's ancestors have been key to unlocking aspects of the past, and have helped in the reconstruction of past climates and environments.

The evolving state of the water vole's teeth through immense periods of geological time, has helped paleontologists, geologists and archeologists to identify cycles of glaciation and warming. Archeologists researching the first human presence in Britain regard the water vole's ancestors as a 'key species' because their evolutionary stages indicate time frames between periods of intense cold and warmer periods when it was possible for early man to survive as hunter-gatherers.[4]

The water vole's presence is evident in fossil records as a species that was able to recolonise in the interglacial periods. This small rodent continued to evolve over at least 2.5 million years while many other mammal species became extinct in northern Europe, including the rhinoceros, the elephant, the hyena, the lion and the woolly mammoth.

---

3) Other extensive finds of fossil mammals from north Norfolk are from later periods and represent fauna of the early Cromerian interglacial 563,000–478,000 years ago.   4) Ashton, Lewis and Stringer, eds., *The Ancient Human Occupation of Britain (Developments in Quaternary Science)* (Amsterdam, 2010).

THE DIFFERENCE BETWEEN SCOTTISH AND ENGLISH WATER VOLES

When the land was covered in tons of ice during the glacials, mammals either perished or migrated south. Populations became established in areas that were not under ice (called refugia) around what is now the Mediterranean, the Balkans, Italy and the Iberian Peninsula. Some populations began to evolve separately over thousands of years of isolation and expanded along different migration routes when the ice retreated. There are slight differences between water voles that survived in different refugia during the last glacial and this is the likely explanation for variation in the northern and southern water voles that occur in Britain today.

In 2004, a group of scientists from the University of Aberdeen used DNA sequencing to examine genetic variation in British water voles.[5] They found significant genetic differences between northern and southern water voles that can be explained by separate evolutionary histories.

Scottish water voles are slightly smaller than those in England and Wales, which are, on average, a little larger than those in Europe. In the north and north-west Highlands of Scotland water voles are mainly black rather than the more typical brown colour. Black or 'melanistic' water voles also occur elsewhere in Britain alongside brown ones. There are other slight differences between southern and northern water voles in the set of the teeth, with the incisors of the Scottish voles being more prominent or 'pro-odont'.

Derek Gow, an ecological consultant specialising in water vole conservation, told me that the exact distribution of both forms is currently unclear and that 'recent genetic studies undertaken by the Northumberland Wildlife Trust suggests that the original type – principally found in Scotland – extends down to the Humber and may well continue far further south than this'.

View north into Sutherland from Coigach. Water voles occur across Scotland but in this remote landscape they have been recorded in recent surveys in surprisingly high densities.

5) In 2004, scientists from the University of Aberdeen explored the evolutionary differences between Scottish (northern) and English and Welsh (southern) water voles by examining DNA from representative samples. They found that while the divergence between the two groups was clear and significant, they could not be classified even as sub-species. The researchers concluded that there were separate evolutionary histories for the Scottish and the English and Welsh water voles, resulting from two phases of post-glacial recolonisation. The Scottish water voles' ancestry could be traced to an Iberian refugium while the English and Welsh came from an eastern European refugium. They concluded that it was likely that the Scottish or northern race water voles were the first migrants, and the second wave took over territory occupied by the first migrants. Piertney, Stewart. Lambin, Telfer, Aars and Dallas, 'Phylogeographic structure and postglacial evolutionary history of water voles (Arvicola terrestris) in the United Kingdom', *Molecular Ecology*, Vol.14, (2005), pp1,435–1,444.

Looking north to Suilven and Ben More Assynt from Stac Pollaidh – a rocky, watery landscape in West Sutherland that is home to the Highland water vole.
In this remote area many small populations function as 'metapopulations' in which individual water voles may travel long distances to disperse.

Most Highland water voles are black in colour unlike this reddish-brown Derbyshire vole.

Derbyshire in the last Ice Age

The Peak District was covered by ice during the Anglian glacial period (470,000–420,000 BP (Before Present)), but during the most recent Ice Age (Devensian 80,000–10,000 BP) ice sheets covered Scotland, the Lake District, the North Pennines and much of Wales. Reaching just to the north-east margins of the Dark Peak, and extending through Cheshire to south Staffordshire on the west, and to York on the east, they reached their maximum extent at different times in different areas.[6]

Climatic conditions in Derbyshire would then have resembled the freezing tundra of present-day Siberia. This was a landscape in which spotted hyena, lynx, lion, cave and brown bear, wolverine, bison, reindeer, woolly rhinoceros and woolly mammoth roamed.[7]

To the north of the county great volumes of meltwater, rocks and boulders from thawing snowfields shaped the current valleys of the Peak District, while the wide, flat valley floors of the Dove and the Trent reflect the flow of glacial meltwater from the west. These river systems are the network of waterways that support our current populations of water voles here in the middle of England.

Mist fills the Derwent valley under Curbar and Froggatt edges.

6) Ford, *Rocks & Scenery of the Peak District* (Ashbourne: Landmark, 2002).   7) Yalden, *The History of British Mammals*.

OPPOSITE PAGE: Bradford Dale, like all the limestone dales of the White Peak, was carved out by water and debris from the receding ice sheets during the interglacials.

THE FIRST FARMERS

Around 12,000 years ago, as the last Ice Age was coming to an end, people migrated northwards into the area that is now Britain. During a period of rapid sea level rise, the land bridge to mainland Europe was lost and Britain became an island around 8,000 years ago. The early Stone Age or Mesolithic (c.10,000 BC–c.4,500 BC) people were previously considered to be nomadic hunter-gatherers who made tools for hunting and carried out minor modifications to their environment, such as burning heather and clearing reedbeds.

It is now thought that they were engaged in complex activities of cultivation and stock management with evidence of settled communities discovered in certain areas of Britain. It is possible that some of the blanket bog that covers much of the Dark Peak began to establish itself after Mesolithic hunters burned off some upland scrub to provide better grazing for their main quarry – red deer. But the main period of clearance of much of the woodland cover of Britain came with the new culture of farming introduced by Neolithic people.

Red deer stag, the main quarry of the Mesolithic hunters, photographed here during the October 'rut' on Big Moor where a herd of around 200 red deer now flourish.

THE NEOLITHIC AGE

The Neolithic Age (c.4,500 BC–c.2,000 BC) introduced farming to Britain as the first cattle, sheep and goats were brought across from mainland Europe by the new migrants. They also brought seeds and tools for cultivation. There was a long period of transition in which the hunter-gatherers of the Mesolithic Age adapted to a new way of life, which involved a more settled existence and far greater impacts on the landscapes and the wildlife of Britain. The new farmers cleared areas of forest and grazed their stock. They developed more complex human communities with buildings, enclosures, communal tombs and evidence of trade, worship and ritual. Neolithic people left their mark in the Peak District with up to 11 longbarrows and 16 chambered tombs and the great henge monument of Arbor Low, the 'Stonehenge of the north'.

THE BRONZE AGE

The Bronze Age people (c.2,000 BC–c.500 BC) discovered the use of metal and control of fire and were able to make complex tools including the first ploughs. By the Middle Bronze Age enclosures are evident, indicating a higher level of management of the land and an increase in population of both humans and grazing stock. There is evidence of increased forest clearance and extensive field systems have been found on the Eastern Moors of the Peak District. The first hill forts were built in the uplands in the late Bronze Age, suggesting a more territorial view of the land. There are numerous Bronze Age sites in Derbyshire confirming the value of this landscape to these early farmers whose tools have been found by their successors over the last few hundred years. Remains of their places of worship and burial are evident throughout the Derbyshire uplands in numerous stone circles and burial mounds or tumuli.

THE IRON AGE

The Iron Age people (c.800 BC–AD 43) worked on the land developing a culture and religion that revolved around the seasons of the farming year. Cereal crops were grown and new types of sheep and cattle were introduced to feed an increasing population. Bigger and heavier iron ploughshares were able to increase cultivation on a larger scale, but the people of the Iron Age made limited incursions into the wilder lands of Britain. There was a newcomer to the pasturelands of Britain in the form of the brown hare (*Lepus europaeus*), which was first introduced by the ancient Britons as a creature of religious and ceremonial significance.

Throughout this long period of widespread and increasing human presence over 8,000 years, the impact on many of Britain's largest animals was devastating. Early extinctions of animals like the elephant, lion, hyena and hippopotamus were caused by the changing climate. As Britain warmed, reindeer and lemmings headed north and eastwards for colder habitats. The total extinctions of the woolly rhinoceros, woolly mammoth and giant Irish elk were most likely caused by human hunting as were the much later extinctions in Britain of the bear, lynx and wolf. Small animals went beneath the notice of man's attention and benefited by the opening up of new habitat and the loss of some predators.

Water voles that do not live near water

Water voles that live on the land are the same species as those that live alongside watercourses but they are called 'fossorial', as they have evolved to live underground in extensive and complex burrow systems. These two distinct ecological forms of the water vole are both present in Continental Europe.

'These two forms differ in their morphology, with the continental aquatic form weighing 150–300 grams, while the fossorial form is smaller at 60–150 grams and has more protruding incisors (more pro-odont). Their behaviour and the habitat used are also different. The aquatic form inhabits rivers, streams and lakes, has stable populations and rarely reaches a density higher than 100 individuals per hectare in wetlands or 15 individuals per 100 metres of riverbank. The fossorial population, on the other hand, occurs in dry grasslands, such as meadows and pastures and lives underground in burrows like a mole. This population shows marked periodic fluctuations with five to eight year cycles and densities of up to a thousand individuals per hectare. They can then cause severe damage to grasslands.' Jefferies, 'The Aquatic and Fossorial Forms of the Water Vole, their History, Evolution, Morphology and Ecology' (2003).[8]

In many parts of mainland Europe there are terrestrial water voles that are classified as agricultural pests as their burrowing activity can cause land to collapse damaging both pastureland and crops. Much of their lives are lived underground and so in addition to eating vegetation, they also eat roots and tubers. Once damage has been done to the roots of a crop it is destroyed and so they are regarded as a major pest in certain parts of France, Germany and Belgium. In these countries considerable effort is put into limiting the expansion of the fossorial water vole as they can increase in numbers dramatically in cyclical population explosions.

Until very recently it was thought that a combination of increasing agricultural intensification and persecution had caused the extinction of the fossorial water vole from mainland Britain by 1900. However remnant colonies were discovered in the 1990s living in small islands and islets in the Sound of Jura on the west coast of Scotland. This relict population of fossorial water voles has been the subject of research into effects on the genetic development of such isolated populations. Finding out just how sustainable isolated populations can be is helping conservationists to understand the point at which isolated groups of voles may no longer be viable.[9]

---

8) In Jeffries, ed., *The Water Vole and Mink Survey of Britain 1996–1998 with a history of the long-term changes in the status of both species and their causes* (Ledbury, 2003). 9) Researchers found that there was a high level of genetic variation between the island populations that had the greatest distance of water between them, whereas there were closer gene matches found between voles on islands that were closer together. They concluded that voles had managed to expand and interbreed by crossing the water despite high tides and currents. While there were signs of mink on one of the islands, the relative security from predators afforded by the islands and unrestricted access to food (as they are not limited to a watercourse) has allowed the population to stabilise with large numbers. Genetic analysis of some of the colonies showed that the isolation had restricted their gene pool, which could make these island colonies self-limiting and more vulnerable to disease. Telfer, Dallas, Aars, Piertney, Stewart and Lambin, 'Demographic and genetic structure of fossorial water voles (Arvicola terrestris) on Scottish Islands' in *Journal of Zoology*, Vol.259 (2003).

OPPOSITE PAGE: Baby water vole in spring.

The voles of the Sound of Jura were thought to be the only extant population of terrestrial water voles in the British Isles, but a colony was recently discovered near Glasgow. Further investigation found an extensive population occupying a 'significant area of urban habitat' in Garthamlock.

'Their habitat typically comprises amenity lawns, roadside verges, wildflower meadows and areas of rough grassland. They commonly live in friable soils amongst tussock grasses and tall ruderal plants (coarse grassland) which provide plenty of food and cover. Burrows may be detected by the molehill-like spoil heaps and runs between the grass. Their tussocks may be marked with large latrines that help confirm the species. It is quite possible that water voles may exhibit this terrestrial behaviour elsewhere in Britain on other sites which have so far been over-looked.' British and Irish Association of Zoos and Aquariums (BIAZA), *Call for Help for Unique Population of Terrestrial Water Voles* (2014).[10]

This find is hugely significant for the mammalogists and conservationists intent on understanding the ecology of the species. There are plans to establish a captive breeding programme to assess the possibilities of reintroduction of the fossorial water vole. The following account from the 9th century seems to refer to the terrestrial water vole – which is surprising, as no trace of the species has been recorded in Ireland since. This could be regarded as a cautionary tale from the past, warning against any future releases into the wild.

'Vermin of a strange species were seen in Ireland, similar to moles, with two long teeth each; and they ate all the corn, all the pasture, and the roots of grasses, and the hay ground, causing a famine in the country, and it is supposed the Pagans took them there, and wished likewise to introduce them into the isle of Britain; but by prayer to God, alms to the poor, and righteous life, God sent a sharp frost during the summer weather, which destroyed those insects.' *Brut y Tywysogion* (Chronicle of the Princes), translated from Welsh of AD 893.

It is likely that these 'strange insects' flourished unnoticed in 9th-century Britain.

10) See [online] <http://www.biaza.org.uk/news/1571/15/Call-for-Help-for-Unique-Population-of-Terrestrial-Water-Voles>

The water vole: the most common mammal in Britain for 3,000 years

WIGBER LOW NEAR ASHBOURNE

Wigber Low is a narrow limestone ridge in the southern part of the White Peak near the village of Kniveton. From this narrow hilltop you can see the distinctive outline of Minninglow (the Neolithic barrow) to the north, and on a clear day the valley of the Trent away to the south. To the west there are wide views of the valley of the Bradbourne stream, and on the eastern side the ridge drops steeply down to another stream. This narrow hilltop was once the site of human habitation before it became a place for burial. Wigber Low had a stone platform on top of a low cairn, on which both Neolithic and Bronze Age people left their dead exposed to the air to be devoured by the carrion birds before the bones of the deceased were buried.

These 'sky burials' were known rituals of the Neolithic and early Bronze Age people, but locating the flat-topped burial platform was a first for the team of archeologists from the University of Sheffield who carried out meticulous excavations of the site in 1975 and 1976. In a bid to get ahead of treasure seekers, the most extensive excavation of any of the numerous ancient burial mounds of Derbyshire was undertaken, funded by the Department of the Environment.

TOP: View north from Wigber Low near Kniveton. BOTTOM: Mound of loose stones forming a broad cairn at Wigber Low in which archaeologists found over 5,000 water vole bones.

In the 19th century, Anglo-Saxon gold, silver and bronze had been excavated at Wigber Low. In the 1970s archeologists found fragments of Neolithic stone axes, pottery, jet beads, Bronze and Iron Age daggers, swords and buckles as well as Roman and mediaeval coins and artefacts. Around and contained within the cairn and below ground were the scattered human bones of Neolithic and Bronze Age burials and partial and whole skeletons revealed an Anglo-Saxon cemetery. By sieving the ground the team also unearthed nearly 15,000 bones of non-food animals, most of which were small rodents and toads (*Bufo bufo*). Of the 7,522 rodent bones, 81 per cent (6,102) were water vole (*Arvicola terrestris/amphibius*) and most of the rest were field vole (*Microtus agrestis*) together with the rare and remarkable find of one beaver (*Castor fiber*). Nearly 4,000 of the water vole bones were found within the cairn itself and many on the old ground surface.[11]

How did they get there, and what does this tell us about how common water voles were through the thousands of years of history recorded on this site? The specialist archeologist on site in the 1970s, Mark Maltby, believed that the presence of so many water voles on Wigber Low 'could be accounted for by their burrowing through the cairn and dropping through the stones and soils … which could explain the abundant finds of their skeletons'. Burrowing fossorial water voles were the more common form of water voles, but the presence of nearly 900 toad bones indicates that another likely source of these remains is the pellets of birds of prey. Buzzards are known to include both toad and voles in their diet. It is easy to imagine crows and buzzards circling above this bleak little hillside or perched like sentinels on the cairn amid the human remains.

Ancient buildings and caves were once the haunts of owls and on open sites like Wigber Low, scavenging raptors such as buzzards and kites were likely to be frequent visitors leaving remnants of small mammals in their pellets. Human dwellings often had wells into which small animals would fall and be unable to escape. These 'pit traps' also exist in rock fissures or mine shafts that reach down to cave systems. Animal remains deposited over millennia help to build a picture of the presence and relative abundance of species in past ages.

Archeological findings of small-mammal fauna from other sites around Britain, while not so spectacular in number as those at Wigber Low, suggest that the water vole was by far the most common mammal in Britain and from the last retreat of the ice through to the Iron Age constituted around half of all the mammals in Britain.[12]

11) Maltby, 'Animal Bones' in Collis, *Wigber Low, Derbyshire: A Bronze Age and Anglian Burial Site in the White Peak* (Sheffield, 1983).   12) Jefferies, 'The Changes in the Population of the Water Vole in Britain, its Size and Constitution since the Last Ice Age', in Jeffries, ed., *The Water Vole and Mink Survey of Britain 1996–1998 with a history of the long-term changes in the status of both species and their causes* (Ledbury, 2003).

DOWEL CAVE

Dowel Cave near Longnor on the Staffordshire border with Derbyshire at the western edge of the White Peak, was used in the Mesolithic, Neolithic, Beaker, Bronze Age, Iron Age and Roman periods. In bone assemblages at Neolithic levels in Dowel Cave, water voles make up 55 per cent of small-mammal fauna with field voles at 34 per cent.[13] Ossom's Eyrie, another cave in the Peak District, was in human use from the early Stone Age and contained the fossil bones of both bison and reindeer as well as some of the earliest finds of water vole.

BILLIONS OF WATER VOLES

Both Ossom's Eyrie and Dowel Cave provided material considered to be 12,000 years old. In 1975, Montgomery studied changes in the sub-fossil remains of water voles in British cave deposits from upper Paleolithic through Roman times to the present. Analysis of sub-fossil skulls and teeth (12,000–2,000 BP) compared to recent samples (1930s) showed that the older voles were much smaller and their teeth much more prominent (pro-odont). Montgomery speculated that these changes represented an evolutionary progression over 12,000 years.[14]

Dowel Cave near Longnor where water vole bones made up over half of the small mammal finds at Neolithic levels.

13) Sub-fossil remains of once-living organisms are those which are either not old enough to have fossilised or were deposited in conditions in which fossilisation would not occur. Sub-fossil remains of vertebrates are often found in caves where they have remained undisturbed for thousands of years. As they contain organic material they can be used for radiocarbon dating, which can provide vital clues to the age of bone assemblages.   14) Montgomery, 'On the relationship between sub-fossil and recent British water voles' in *Mammal Review*, Vol.5, No.1 (1975), pp23–29.

However Strachan and Jefferies from the Vincent Wildlife Trust propose another explanation – that the large aquatic water vole was present at the same time as the smaller fossorial water vole. Both of these occurred in much greater numbers in the distant past. Strachan and Jefferies suggest that in the late Iron Age, the water voles that lived on the land (fossorial) outnumbered the aquatic voles by 29 to 1. They worked out a figure for the population of all water voles living in pre-Roman Britain as well over 6.5 billion.[15]

Throughout the Mesolithic, Neolithic, Bronze and Iron Ages the fossorial water vole persisted as the principal grazing animal of the grasslands of Britain and the commonest mammal by far. The first farmers created ideal conditions for the water vole by clearing much of the forest cover of Britain, and opening up vast areas of pasture, which was the principal habitat for this burrowing vole.

It appears that there was little change in the numbers of water voles from the end of the last Ice Age until the late Iron Age, but around 200 BC there was a sudden and dramatic change in the population of water voles that lived both in and out of the water in Britain.

THE DECLINE AND FALL OF THE ROMAN WATER VOLE

'The water vole population "crashed" from being the most common mammal in Britain to around a tenth of its original percentage presence in only 600 years … This crash started in the late Iron Age at 2200 years BP (200 BC) and it continued throughout the Romano-British period up to 1600 years BP (AD 400) before the decline curve flattened out.' Jefferies, 'The Changes in the Population of the Water Vole in Britain, its Size and Constitution since the Last Ice Age' (2003).[16]

During the relatively short period of the Roman occupation (AD 43–410) Britain was changed from an agricultural, rural society with regional tribal power structures to a centrally administered, military and legal outpost of the Roman Empire. Britain's landscape was already extensively cleared

---

15) To get a picture of the relative proportions of both kinds of water voles Jefferies worked out the full extent of riparian habitat available to water voles in pre-Roman Britain at the maximum possible levels of occupancy (as determined by highest levels found in the British National Water Vole surveys). It was shown by Harris et al. in 1995 that the total length of watercourse available to water voles in mainland Britain was 294,938 kilometres. By removing the length of canals built in recent times and by doubling lengths of rivers to allow for both banks Jefferies multiplied 326,403 kilometres x 27.434 water voles per kilometre. He added in extensive marsh areas (in existence during the Iron Age) that were prime habitat for aquatic water voles and arrived at a summer optimum number of aquatic water voles living in pre-Roman Britain of over 225,000 million. This enormous figure is then dwarfed when viewed against overall population of all water voles (largely made up terrestrial voles) which Jefferies put at around 6.8 billion, or more precisely this: 6,757,397,709. Jefferies, 'Changes in the Population of the Water Vole in Britain', p142.   16) In Jefferies, ed., *The Water Vole and Mink Survey of Britain 1996–1998 with a history of the long-term changes in the status of both species and their causes* (Ledbury, 2003).

and farmed with small settled communities living close to their means of subsistence, but the Romans brought new crops, more productive seeds, new kinds of livestock and new technologies to intensify farming. The human population of Britain increased from around 250,000 at the time of the invasion to around 3.5 million at the height of the occupation. The Romans built roads and developed towns with large populations that needed feeding through more intensive farming.

The diet of the Romans was cereal based, so they increased arable planting and drained large areas of marsh for cultivation. Grain drove the economy of Roman Britain, and what surplus farmers could grow was either requisitioned by the legions or sold in the new moneyed economy of Britain. This led to increasing levels of intensive farming and a drive to cultivate areas only marginally appropriate for agriculture – especially in the north and west. The Romans' insatiable need for grain for human and animal food and for revenue pushed the land to its limits. Numbers of grazing stock also increased to feed a much bigger population.

'The Romans not only continued and intensified the existing agricultural system in Britain, they also expanded agriculture into new areas and introduced new technologies and methods. As a consequence, the landscape became more vulnerable to environmental change. On this fully exploited landscape fell the weight of climatic deterioration.' Jones, *The End of Roman Britain* (New York, 1996), pp202–203.

This sounds similar both in cause and effect to the environmental problems facing Britain and the rest of the world today. Towards the end of the Roman occupation, a colder and wetter period began and the land reclamation works undertaken by the Romans disrupted the processes of natural drainage, causing widespread flooding across south and south-east England. A profoundly altered and degraded natural environment had been over-grazed by an increased number of cattle and sheep. This goes some way to explaining the crash in water vole numbers.

'Erosion caused by the delayed but cumulative effects of generations of forest clearance, grazing, and ploughing probably intensified the natural environmental problems by contributing to flooding and silting.' Jones, *The End of Roman Britain*.

The evidence for the population crash is revealed in small-mammal fauna data found at archeological sites and compiled by Derek Yalden. Jefferies estimates that the drop of water vole numbers from 46.98 per cent of small-mammal fauna to 4.49 per cent is even greater numerically than those figures suggest as there was a much-reduced population of all small mammals by AD 400.

The impact of large grazing animals on small-mammal fauna is immense and central to any understanding of the demise of the water vole, both aquatic and terrestrial.

A young water vole peers out across feeding remains at the water's edge.

Water vole on an island in a limestone stream surrounded by false watercress.

The 'Dark Ages'

In the 600 years following the withdrawal of the Roman legions from Britain in AD 410 much of the great farming enterprise of the previous centuries came to a grinding halt as the country faced invasions from first the Saxons, then the Vikings and Danish.

By the time of the Domesday Book (1086), most of the much-reduced human population (around 2 million) lived in the countryside, so with fewer non-productive urban dwellers the need for intensive farming lessened. Wheat and other grains were important for both human and animal consumption but cereal crops had low yields, and so needed considerable acreage with less spare for grazing. With diminished numbers of cattle and sheep and fewer people to eat them, pastures went back to the wild. As the population of humans contracted, populations of small mammals appear to have stabilised until the next great impact on the landscapes of Britain that came with the sheep ranches of the monastic grange farms.

The Middle Ages in the Peak District

'Sheep have eaten up our meadows and our downs, our corn, our wood, whole villages and towns.'
16th-century epigram.

'Taming the landscape and exploiting its pastures for grazing sheep and cultivating crops, was the major enterprise of the monasteries, which managed the land and developed new techniques in farming throughout the Middle Ages until the Dissolution in the 1530s.

'The Cistercian order, whose pioneering methods of land management were gradually adopted by other religious orders … exploited the marginal, undeveloped lands away from the settled areas of Europe and they became the great sheep-farmers of England. They were a pioneer force, intent on colonising the wilds of such upland areas as the Peak District. The extensive limestone heath and coarse vegetation of the uplands was fit only for sheep, the wool and meat of which were immensely valuable to the economy of the times. Packhorses would have taken the wool from the remote areas of the White Peak along the ancient trackways and trading routes that existed at this time. Some wool would be taken along routes that led east towards the Humber for shipping to Europe. At this time English wool was a major export and great profits were made from this and from other surplus products (such as corn or meat).'
Gregory, *A River in Time* (Bakewell, 2013).

In the middle of the 14th century the Black Death killed between a third and a half of the population of Britain, but the depopulation of much of the country did not impede the growth of sheep farming, as sheep are not labour intensive. Wool was the driving force of the British economy, creating vast wealth for the monasteries and other landowners. It has been estimated that in AD 1500 there were 8 million sheep. There were three sheep for every person in Britain, and the national flock was growing to what some have estimated as 12 million in the late 15th and 16th centuries. In a passage of Thomas More's *Utopia* (1516) he wrote, 'Sheep have become so great devourers and so wild, that they eat up and down the very men themselves. They consume, destroy and devour whole fields, houses and cities.'

The Tudors and Stuarts

The Tudor and Stuart periods introduced further great changes to the landscape and wildlife of England and Wales through agriculture. Forests were cleared, wetlands were drained and land reclaimed from the sea. This was also a period in which the persecution of wild animals became more systematic and the destruction of wildlife became enshrined in law. Almost every wild animal in Britain had a price on its head and was hunted for payment, food, sport, fur or feathers. Many species were regarded as vermin or pests competing with humans for the limited resources available.

During the reigns of both Henry VIII and then Queen Elizabeth I, poor harvests, and later on the severe winters of Britain's 'Little Ice Age', meant a scarcity of food and wild animals were regarded as competitors. Laws were passed to make it the responsibility of landowners and all communities of more than ten households 'to kill and utterly distroye all manner of Choughes, Crowes and Rookes'.[17] Later, Elizabeth I strengthened this Act in 1566 to include a wide range of named species, most of which had no impact on cereal crops. This Act, which was not repealed until 1863, had devastating and far-reaching consequences for the wildlife of England and Wales.

Roger Lovegrove, naturalist and former director of the Royal Society for the Protection of Birds for Wales, spent six years researching the historic persecution of British wildlife and in doing so searched through parish records from all over England and Wales to assess the impact of the systematic slaughter of many of our most loved and now endangered species. His book, *Silent Fields*, published in 2006, makes grim but essential reading for anyone with an interest in British wildlife.

The list of targeted species from the 1566 Act includes:

All members of the crow family, starling, most birds of prey, woodpecker, kingfisher, dipper (thought then to be the female kingfisher), bullfinch, fox, badger, pine marten, polecat, weasel, stoat, wildcat, otter, hedgehog, rat, mouse and mole.

The Act of 1566 required that funds were raised through a levy of all landowners, farmers and tenants. The funds were then administered in each parish by churchwardens and other worthy persons, who paid out bounties for each type of animal. There are few early records of these payments, as they were initially not part of the parish records. The bulk of records examined by Roger Lovegrove were made in the later part of the 17th century and then throughout the 18th century. This suggests that the project of extermination initiated by Queen Elizabeth gained greater momentum through time, and was extended informally to include almost any species the parish fancied killing.

---

17) Henry VIII introduced the first of a series of Acts in 1532 that were followed by those of his daughter Elizabeth I. They are known collectively as the Tudor Vermin Acts.

It is not surprising that the water vole made its way on to the hit list. Roger Lovegrove has uncovered records from three parishes in Dorset where churchwardens paid out money for large numbers of rats killed (at Sherbourne over 9,000 in one year) from the mid to late 18th century and again in the early part of the 19th century. The common rat (*Rattus norvegicus*) did not arrive on these shores until 1720 and the black rat or 'ship rat' was confined to seaports. It is not possible that the common rat could have spread so far and bred to this extent in so few years. Lovegrove surmises that both the later Dorset 'rats' and the rats initially targeted by the Tudor Vermin Acts must have been water voles. Before the arrival of the common rat, the black rat was certainly a threat to grain stores in coastal settlements and the water vole was a cause of considerable damage to arable and grazing land in ways that it is now hard for us to imagine.

Gilbert White, the great 18th-century naturalist, began to suspect that two forms of water vole existed in Britain at the time he wrote the following letter to his friend Thomas Pennant:

'I suspect much that there may be two species of water-rats … Now I have discovered a rat on the banks of our little stream that is not web-footed, and yet is an excellent swimmer and diver and answers exactly to the mus amphibious of Linnaeus … [who] seems to be in a puzzle about his mus amphibious, and to doubt whether it differs from his mus terrestris.' Rev. Gilbert White, Letter 10 to Thomas Pennant, Esq., Selbourne, 4 August 1767.

Two and half years later, in another letter to Pennant, he appears to have found the 'mus terrestris' but still identifies it as a 'water rat':

'As a neighbor was lately ploughing in a dry chalky field, far removed from any water, he turned out a water rat, that was curiously laid up in an hibernaculum artificially formed of grass and leaves. At one end of the burrow lay above a gallon of potatoes regularly stowed, on which it was to have supported itself for the winter. But the difficulty with me is how this 'amphibious mus' came to fix its winter station at such a distance from the water. Was it determined in its choice of that place by the mere accident of finding the potatoes which were planted there; or is it the constant practice of the aquatic rat to forsake the neighbourhood of the water in the colder months?'
Rev. Gilbert White, Letter 26 to Thomas Pennant, Esq., Selbourne, 8 December 1769.

Water vole plague

In 1896 a 'water vole plague' on Read's Island in the Humber Estuary is said to have caused massive damage to banks and coastal defenses and involved a campaign of extermination. According to a contemporary account from the *Eastern Morning News*, Read's Island 'is burrowed from end to end, and so densely populated … that it is almost impossible to put a foot down without standing on a rat-hole. The entire island is as brown and rough as a ploughed field and there now exists scarce sufficient pasture to feed one rabbit.' The island was flooded by cutting into the earth banks and 'as the water advanced the rats fled from their holes in tens and hundreds of thousands and made for the banks which remained high and dry'. After this a shooting party was organised, then the remaining voles either starved or attempted to swim across the Humber estuary to the mainland.

The population explosion and the extensive tunneling activities of the Read's Island voles point to one of the last records for Britain's terrestrial water voles, and by around 1900 it had seemed that they were extinct.

It is tempting to think that following persecution here in Britain of our fossorial water voles they took to the water in order to survive. But as there have been no extant fossorial water voles to study on mainland Britain until very recently, we really don't know the relationship between these 'same' animals that live so differently either in the water or under the ground.

Early water vole species existed in our part of the world when the climate was almost tropical, whereas later species evolved between periods when the land was under ice or permafrost. It was present while climate conditions in Britain resembled Arctic tundra and the woolly mammoth and early man first roamed Britain half a million years ago, but in the easy climate conditions of our present interglacial it is poised on the brink of extinction. The scale of the water vole's population collapse is unprecedented. Feral American mink are commonly considered to be the main culprit in the decline of the water vole, but they come very late into a much bigger picture of long-term decline.

Changes in land use in the 20th century

It is difficult to form a picture of any connection between the grazing needs of the large and heavy herbivores sheep and cattle, and those of a small rodent; the water vole. It is clearly an unequal contest. But it is precisely this unequal competition for resources between livestock and the water vole that was the principal cause of the population collapse in Roman times and which had driven this mammal to the final stage of its decline as early as 1900.

'The reduction in numbers had amounted to 99.48% over a century ago by which time the unbroken lines of occupied river bank had begun to disintegrate into separate colonies with gaps like beads on a string.'

When Donald Jefferies wrote the conclusion to the report of the *Water Vole and Mink Survey of Britain* in 2003 there had been no evidence of the terrestrial water vole since the 1920s and the aquatic water vole's range was shrinking fast.

'The water vole population had almost disappeared from the uplands of northern and western England and Wales by the mid-twentieth century (Strachan and Jefferies, 1993) and at the end of that century even the south eastern population appeared to be breaking up into smaller and smaller occupied areas.'

A large herd of Swaledale sheep (an upland breed) in gathering pens before their release on to adjoining moorland.

THE IMPACT OF SHEEP

As we have seen, sheep were the driving force of the British economy through the Middle Ages with wool being exported all over Europe. Sheep shaped much of the landscape that we know today through the clearance of woodlands, the grazing of uplands and the draining of vast swathes of marshland including coastal marshes. The number of sheep has been increasing since the Iron Age, and reached record numbers in 1992 with nearly 45 million in the UK.[18]

After the foot-and-mouth disease outbreak of 2001 there was a sharp decline and the current population stands at around 23 million.[19]

18) UK Livestock Numbers, *MeatStats 8* (August 2014).   19) Defra, *Farming statistics: livestock populations at 1 December 2013*, (London, 2014).

Aside from the massive increases in the 1990s, overall sheep numbers have not increased much over the last 150 years. However their regional distribution has altered radically since the interwar years. In the late 1930s there was a break-up of much of the farming landscape, as many large estates sold off their tenant farms, and with them went the patchwork pattern of the Victorian era in which crops were rotated and both sheep and cattle moved around pastures through the year. Mixed farming gave way to more intensified farming systems and a split between arable and stock farming. This led to the increased polarisation of farming areas so that arable farming became more concentrated in the drier and warmer south and east of Britain while sheep and cattle farming became more concentrated in the cooler, wetter north and west.

In the 1980s, suspecting a serious decline in water vole numbers, Jefferies, Morris and Mulleneux searched through local natural history literature to find records of localities occupied by water voles in England, Wales and Scotland. They searched 180 different journals as well as 50 monographs, to find 2,635 records from 1900–1985 (73 per cent of which were recorded from 1939–1979). They then compared their records of water vole presence with figures from the sheep censuses of 1874, 1938 and 1966. While the numbers of sheep had not changed significantly, at around 29 million at each of those dates, the parts of Britain in which sheep were concentrated had changed completely. They discovered a clear correlation between the densities of sheep and the absence or scarcity of water voles. Low records of water voles were found in Wales, the north of England and most of Scotland. Where sheep were, water voles weren't.[20]

The polarisation of farming activity established in the interwar years has prevailed through to today, and though stocking levels of uplands have decreased considerably in more recent years, regional losses of water vole populations continue to be associated with high sheep densities.

Sheep graze very close to the ground, and will crop right up to the edges of vegetation growing on the banks of rivers, streams and ditches. By doing so they reduce both food sources and some of the dense, layered cover of plants that water voles depend on, leaving just narrow margins of vegetation at the very edge of the water. This reduces the overall width of suitable habitat along watercourses and leaves water voles more vulnerable to predation by aerial predators as well as foxes, stoats and weasels, and, of course, mink.

SHEEP IN THE UPLANDS

In 1946, in a drive to use marginal lands for livestock farming, the Hill Farming Act made grants available to improve upland farms. This caused a massive expansion of livestock farming in uplands. In 1972, the UK joined the Common Market, and in 1976 the Hill Livestock (Compensatory Allowances) regulations were introduced which provided European funding for hill farmers based on number of stock.

---

20) Jefferies, Morris, & Mulleneux, 'An enquiry into the changing status of the water vole Arvicola terrestris in Britain' in *Mammal Review*, Vol.19, No.3 (1989), p111–131. See also data maps on pages 192 and 193.

A study by Derek Yalden showed the extent of increased stocking in upland pastures in the Peak District. An average of 16.483 sheep on 23,709 hectares in the early 1930s had trebled to 48,966 by the mid 1970s. In other areas, increased planting of forestry in upland areas restricted the available land, so that over-stocking had an even higher impact on the landscape and wildlife.

Sheep can be immensely destructive to upland habitats, not only denuding the riparian plant species that water voles depend on but also reducing biodiversity of moorland by stripping out heather, bilberry and many other upland plant species. Herbaceous plants are also eliminated so that certain grasses and sedges dominate and more areas come under bracken. Sheep sometimes damage the nests of upland waders such as lapwing, curlew and snipe by trampling on nests and eggs and compacting the ground, affecting invertebrates that are food for wader species and black grouse.

In upland streams the range and quantity of plant species is limited, and the stretches of suitable water vole habitat are few and often far between. Upland water vole populations are usually small and isolated so that the lack of continuous lengths of suitable habitat makes them more vulnerable when moving about within their home range or when dispersing. Where sheep exist in high densities they can trample heavily around streams (which are their water source and are often forded by them) thereby damaging banksides and compacting the soil, making it harder for voles to burrow.

In the 1940s sheep were being treated with organochlorine insecticides. DDT was replaced with Dieldrin in

the 1950s. These chemicals are toxic to rodents and run-off into upland streams would have been damaging to all wildlife, but the impact on upland water voles was not noticed as no one had realised that they were there in the first place. It has only been understood in recent years just how important upland populations of water voles are to the continuing survival of the species in Britain.

Stocking levels have now been greatly reduced and there are many agencies now involved in improving upland habitat in recognition of the immense value of these areas, not only to wildlife, but as water collection, flood protection and carbon sinks. However, as subsidies for upland farmers have been heavily reduced under current agreements, there may be less incentive for them to work in more environmentally sensitive ways.

part 6

The Otter, the Mink and the Water Vole

The otter has become an iconic symbol of the conservation movement, signalling both the successful clean-up of British rivers and a new culture of understanding and sympathy for wild creatures. But while the otter was disappearing during the four decades from the late 1950s to the early 1990s, its place as the top riparian predator was being taken over by the alien American mink, with disastrous consequences for the water vole.

The otter, the mink and the water vole

'But the poor Fish have enemies enough besides such unnatural Fisher-men, as namely, the Otters that I spake of, the Cormorant, the Bitterne, the Osprey, the Sea-gull, the Herne, the King-fisher, the Gorrara, the Puet, the Swan, Goose, Ducks, and the Craber, which some call the Water-rat: against all which any honest man may make a just quarrel, but I will not, I will leave them to be quarrelled with, and kil'd by others; for I am not of a cruel nature, I love to kill nothing but Fish.'

Izaak Walton, *The Compleat Angler: Or, the Contemplative Man's Recreation* (fourth edition, 1668).

The complex connection between the otter, the mink and the water vole has been the subject of much research and speculation over recent years, but that there is a vital connection is in no doubt. To put it very simply, the otter (*Lutra lutra*) disappeared completely from lowland rivers at the very same time that American mink (*Neovison vison*) began to expand and colonise Britain. Mink found no competition and so were able to take over the territory formerly occupied by the otter.

The water vole is low down the food chain and has a numerous and wide range of predators, which include heron, barn owl, tawny owl, kestrel, buzzard, hen harrier and marsh harrier, pike, fox, otter, polecat, stoat, weasel, domestic cat and brown rat. This long and varied list appears to leave this vulnerable animal with few chances, but water voles had coexisted with native predators over millennia despite great reduction in numbers due to competition for resources with other grazing animals, and to lost habitat. However, the pervasive presence of mink along almost every waterway in Britain has destroyed a balance that allowed the aquatic water vole to maintain its status as a 'common' animal even up until 1990.

This part of the book looks at the changing fortunes of the otter, the mink and the water vole, and also at the role that people have played in altering the delicate balance and interplay between our native wild creatures and their environment.

OPPOSITE PAGE: The Eurasian otter (*Lutra lutra*) depicted in this part of the book was photographed at the Chestnut Centre near Chapel-en-le-Frith.

A nation of nature lovers

In the first half of the 20th century a kind of accommodation and tolerance of British wildlife had been achieved. While hunting with packs of dogs continued, attitudes to wildlife generally were changing. The First World War had a major impact on gamekeepers. The national census of 1911 showed a total of 23,056 gamekeepers in England, Scotland and Wales. One estimate suggests that of the 20,000 gamekeepers that fought in the trenches only 5,000 went back to work as keepers on British estates. The other 15,000 were either killed, injured, lost or changed their jobs as many estates were broken up or made economies between the wars.

In 1981, according to one estimate, there were around 3,500 gamekeepers in Britain.[1] This meant that many species formerly persecuted by gamekeepers began to make recoveries – including the otter. As their numbers increased, they were then targeted with renewed vigour by hunting packs after the Second World War.

Between 1950 and 1955, 13 British packs of otter hounds killed 1,212 otters.[2] However, outside of the worlds of shooting and hunting, the First World War and later the Second World War saw attitudes and sensibilities change. Many experienced a need to connect to the smaller lives being lived all around us, from sparrows and robins in the garden to the badgers in the woods.

Wildfowlers became conservationists and egg collectors became birdwatchers; amateur naturalists became the champions of wildlife. The Royal Society for the Protection of Birds (RSPB), founded in 1889, opened its first reserves in the 1930s. The Wildlife Trusts were founded in 1912 as the Society for the Promotion of Nature Reserves. The British Trust for Ornithology (BTO) was founded in 1933, and in 1946 former wildfowler Sir Peter Scott opened Slimbridge, the first Wildfowl and Wetlands Trust (WWT) reserve.

Grey heron.

1) Tapper, *Game heritage; an ecological review of shooting and gamekeeping records* (Fordingbridge, 1992).   2) Lovegrove, *Silent Fields: The long decline of a nation's wildlife* (Oxford, 2007), p248.

Mammals are more elusive than birds, and most are nocturnal, so they never quite reached the level of following that saw the flourishing success of the RSPB, BTO and WWT. But mammals have their strong support base too, and a following greatly encouraged by the work of the Wildlife Trusts and The Mammal Society, as well as numerous wildlife programmes on television. Public awareness of, and sympathy for, the otter owed much

to the contribution of such writers as Kenneth Grahame in the early part of the century with *The Wind in the Willows* (1908), followed by Henry Williamson's *Tarka the Otter* (1927), and much later, Gavin Maxwell's *Ring of Bright Water* (1960). These works all helped to create an imaginative identification with the charismatic otter after thousands of years of relentless persecution.

The British love affair with wildlife has become part of popular culture and is globally unique. But just as this love affair was becoming established in the latter half of the 20th century, our countryside was being threatened as many of our farmland ecosystems were being damaged, our rivers polluted and mink expanded their range across Britain.

Grey wagtail.

Dipper.

Kingfisher.

Dabchick.

Farming after the Second World War

Post-war Britain underwent an agricultural revolution. Some aspects of this had been set in motion during the war, with the drive to keep Britain self-sufficient and the country fed. The level of government involvement in farming through training, investment, inspection and monitoring continued after the war, along with the introduction of new technologies and the input of a range of chemicals aimed at getting more from the land. The agri-chemical industry was expanding rapidly, agricultural machinery was getting bigger and British farmland was being transformed from a patchwork pattern of mixed farms to wide open spaces in which mono-culture crops were planted, or where large herds of new breeds of cattle roamed over vast fields of 'improved' pasture.

Miles of hedges were being grubbed up, land was drained, and hay meadows ploughed up and replanted with silage grasses. Semi-natural vegetation was lost alongside many watercourses, resulting in ever-increasing fragmentation of riparian habitat. In the meantime a chemical war on insects was being waged from which our rivers and their catchments are only just beginning to recover. It is in this context that the otter declined, mink increased, and the water vole's future lay in the balance.

River Derwent, looking north-west towards the Haddon Estate.

Poisoned rivers

After the Second World War, DDT was in widespread agricultural use. Later, other organochlorine insecticides such as Aldrin and, closely related, Dieldrin were developed to replace DDT and used extensively as agricultural pesticides both in seed dressings and in sheep dip. These highly toxic chemicals leached off the land and into the river systems and, sometimes, excess chemicals were simply emptied into watercourses.

In a decade, toxins released into the environment took several species to the brink of extinction. Peregrine and sparrowhawk that prey on small species of insect and seed-eating birds and mammals nearly died out at the same time as otter numbers crashed both through direct poisoning and reproductive failure. While DDT was still in use, these birds and some other raptors lost the ability to reproduce, as their eggs had shells that would not harden, and so their populations collapsed due to chemical effects on their reproductive systems.

Some toxins that make their way into river systems become more concentrated as they are ingested – a process called bioaccumulation. These toxins move up through the food chain from the invertebrates that fish feed on, to the fish, then to the predator at the top of the chain – the otter. The levels of these chemicals and other substances such as lead (used as an anti-fungicide in seed dressings) could reach lethal levels, but it is likely that before these concentrations were reached in the body tissue of otters, their reproductive capacity had already been severely impaired. By the mid 1970s our poisoned rivers could no longer support otters throughout much of lowland Britain.

In time, the damaging effects of organochlorine insecticides on wildlife and also the potential effects on human health were understood and Dieldrin was gradually withdrawn from use until it was finally banned in 1989. As these chemicals were banned, other sources of pollution were also analysed. Greater attention was being paid to water quality in our rivers and coastal waters. A major clean up of our rivers began in the 1990s, and industrial waste, sewage outflow and effluent from farms were monitored and dealt with as environmental management priorities. The Water Framework Directive (2000), brought in by the European Union, imposes a legal duty on the UK government to clean up our rivers, lakes and streams.

The otter is a highly adapted aquatic animal. It has a long, streamlined, muscular body and is able to dive and swim under water at great speed. It can change direction with ease when swimming by twisting its sinuous body using its tail as a rudder and its large webbed feet as paddles. It can stay below water for as long as 45 seconds. The otter's thick coat provides effective thermal insulation with a shaggy outer layer of long guard hairs that allow water to stream off it without penetrating to the extremely dense, insulating inner layer of fine hairs.

Otter (*Lutra lutra*)

The European or Eurasian otter is in the family of animals called mustelids, which also includes such UK native species as badger, stoat, weasel, polecat and pine marten. The otter's diet consists principally of fish (70 to 95 per cent) but they can adapt to whatever prey is available. Crayfish, amphibians, birds such as coot, moorhen and duck, and mammals including rabbit, rat, mouse and water vole can form part of the otter's diet. Otters need to consume between one and one and half kilograms daily. They are top of the food chain with no native predators other than man.

A female can produce one litter a year of two to three cubs. Baby otters (cubs) are highly dependent on their mothers, whose care they depend on long after they are weaned at 14 weeks. The male has no role in the rearing of young. The female trains her cubs to forage, fish and hunt until they are able to fend for themselves at around ten months. There is a high mortality rate of young otters with only a third surviving past their second year.

Young males are usually the first to disperse and may travel great distances to find new territory, making them especially vulnerable to road traffic.

The otter has been regarded as a competitor and hunted continuously since the arrival of Mesolithic man. It was hunted for recreation from the Middle Ages onwards and persecuted as vermin under the Tudor Vermin Acts. Specialist packs of otter hounds continued to hunt the otter, while game-keepers and river bailiffs shot and trapped them with impunity, until they attained full protection under both Schedule 5 and 6 of the Wildlife and Countryside Act of 1981. It was the otter-hunting fraternity that first noticed that something was amiss, when they found fewer and fewer otters to hunt and kill from the late 1950s onwards. Throughout the 1960s and 1970s otters were beginning to disappear from all the major river systems of south and central England and Wales. They maintained a presence in central Wales and continued to thrive in much

of Scotland, but were extinct in the south of Scotland and most of England and Wales. The first national otter survey in 1977–1979 found evidence of otters in less than six per cent of the sites surveyed in England. The Scottish Highlands remained the stronghold of the otter, despite ongoing persecution by gamekeepers, river bailiffs and fisheries, while it was pushed to the brink of extinction elsewhere.[3]

As the water quality of many of our rivers improved through the 1990s and the otter was legally protected, it began to make a comeback. The recovery was rapid in some areas, particularly in the west, but some regions were too distant from recovering and expanding populations, so captive-bred otters were reintroduced in Cambridgeshire, East Anglia, the Thames and the lower Trent. The otter is now present in every county in England and increasing in numbers.

---

3) At a time when otters were becoming extinct throughout much of lowland Britain I had the shocking experience in 1973 of accompanying a salmon fisherman on a walk along the cliffs of Enard Bay in Wester Ross. The fisherman carried a gun to shoot any otter that might rob his nets of the prize wild salmon which were due – once caught and packed in ice – for the night train to London and the Harrods fish counter.

DERBYSHIRE'S OTTERS

In 1829, Derbyshire historian Steven Glover noted that the otter was 'frequently found in the Trent, Derwent and the smaller rivers communicating with them'. Glover, *The History, Gazetteer and Directory of the County of Derby.*

Most references to the otter from Jourdain in *The Victoria History of the County of Derby* (1905) are of shootings by a mix of landowners, country vicars and gamekeepers. Parts of the Dove offered a safe haven for otters, due to the protection or tolerance of some riparian owners. He notes that in parts of the Dove valley, 'they are so numerous as many as eight have been seen by the keeper in one day'. Most 19th-century records of otters were along the Trent and the Dove while the otter was scarce along the Derwent. It is principally to these three rivers in the south of Derbyshire that the otter has now returned.

The otter had disappeared altogether from Derbyshire in the 1960s to 1970s and no otters were recorded in the county, or in any part of the Midlands, during the first national otter survey of England in 1977–1979. The first positive evidence of otter presence in Derbyshire was spraint found on the River Derwent below Shining Cliff Woods in the early 1990s.[4]

Later on, surveyors recorded spraints in the Dove and Derwent catchments in 1993 and 1994 and a young otter was found dead on the road near South Wingfield, close to the River Amber.[5] Other records were collected in the late 1990s, and in 2000 Derbyshire Wildlife Trust began collecting records systematically through its otter monitoring programme (part of the Water for Wildlife project). It is not possible to assess the population of otters in the county as their range is considerable and may extend as far as 50 kilometres for a male and between 20 and 40 kilometres for a female.

Otters that live in our river systems (riverine otters) are mainly nocturnal, as many of the fish they hunt such as salmon, trout and grayling (the salmonids), slow down at night and are therefore easier to catch. By hunting at night they can also avoid their historic enemy – people.

Otters have been increasing in Derbyshire since 2000, especially in the Dove and the Derwent. They are also present in the Trent, but with fewer signs. In 2014, 30 sites in Derbyshire were monitored regularly and otter presence was confirmed at 22 of them. Four otters were seen alive in the county in 2014 and two were seen swimming together on the River Wye in 2015. Sadly, road casualties now account for many otter deaths in Britain; a dead otter was found on the A38 north of Derby in October 2014 and another near Tansley in March 2015. Several otter ledges have been put in under bridges liable to flood to try and prevent otter road casualties.

---

4) Spraints (faeces) are scent-marked and left at prominent places along the waterside range as a means of communication between otters. They are also vital clues in detecting and recording otter presence.   **5)** Perkins, 'Otter Lutra lutra: Distribution and Status in Derbyshire', in Mallon, Alston and Whiteley, *The Mammals of Derbyshire* (2012)

The otter has returned to Derbyshire unaided by any reintroduction programme and its presence in the county is testament to the increasing health of our rivers and a symbol of hope for the future. But the chances of seeing one are slim as river keeper Warren Slaney explains:

'An otter will stick to the river and move quickly through. In the winter it takes an otter about a week to get through our three and a half miles of the Derwent and sometimes it's even quicker. I don't think they waste their time. They've got so much food with the crayfish and the fish.'

American mink

American mink (*Neovison vison*) is a non-native species of mustelid that was first introduced into Britain in the late 1920s for commercial fur farming.

Most of the feral mink living in Britain are a dark brown 'plain chocolate' colour with white patches around the face. The adult male's combined head and body measures between 33 and 45 centimetres with a bushy tail that is around half that length. The adult female is a little smaller at 32 to 36 centimetres with a correspondingly shorter tail.

Mink living inland tend to be nocturnal or crepuscular (active at dusk). Their presence can be detected by their faeces (known as scats), which are dark green, brown or almost black and five to eight centimetres long with tapered ends. These have a powerfully unpleasant odour, unlike otter spraints which are surprisingly quite fragrant.

Mink are opportunist predators that consume fish, birds and mammals in roughly equal proportions. As they eat a smaller proportion of fish, they did not suffer from the same effects of organochlorine residues that had proved so devastating to the otter. They are semi-aquatic, occupying inland watercourses as well as coastal regions, but they will also adapt to farmland depending on food supply. They mainly favour rivers, streams, canals and lakesides where they will make use of tree roots, rocks, scrub or densely covered banksides for their dens. Like the water vole and the otter their home range is linear, as they tend to stay close to the water's edge. Ranges are between one and six kilometres, with males ranging over further distances than females, but they will focus where prey is plentiful. Mink are able to dive and swim well, although they are not especially adapted to an aquatic environment in the ways that otters are. Mink are fierce predators but they are also predated themselves by golden eagle, badger and otter.

OPPOSITE PAGE: American mink (*Neovison vison*) photographed on the shore near Ardnamurchan Point, the most westerly part of mainland Britain, in Lochaber, West Highlands. THIS PAGE, TOP: Mink scats are cylindrical with tapered ends measuring five to eight centimetres, and usually one centimetre in diameter. BOTTOM: These five-toed footprints found on a moorland track belong to a medium-sized mustelid; either mink, feral ferret or polecat. Mink prints measure two and a half to four centimetres long, and two to four centimetres wide, and when found on soft mud by watercourses are often seen in a characteristic splayed 'star' shape. While a good indication of mink presence, neither footprints nor scats are diagnostic signs.

The female produces one litter with between four and six kits, usually in May. Lactation lasts for six to eight weeks. Young mink are able to breed the year after they are born and disperse around ten kilometres from their birthplace – hence the rapid spread of the species along our waterways.

Although otters are known to hunt and kill water voles, and their speed and high level of adaptation as marine mammals make water voles easy meat for them, the proportion of water vole in the otter diet is very small. However, the female mink is a specialist, being exactly the size that makes it possible for her to enter and raid a water vole's burrow taking both adult and baby water voles. For a nursing female mink, a colony of water voles represents a very convenient food source. She can simply help herself on a nightly basis to both baby and adult voles, thereby depleting or destroying a whole colony of voles in the course of one summer. When juvenile mink are able to hunt at around five to seven months in the autumn and through the winter, owing to their smaller size they are particularly dangerous to a much reduced, overwintering population of water voles. These are the precious breeding animals that might sustain a population. The spring population of water voles is just 30 per cent of the summer/autumn population so if this number is depleted further it is easy to see why local water vole extinctions frequently follow mink occupation of their habitat. It seems that mink actively seek out water voles and target them as a primary food source.

The national water vole and mink surveys (1989–1990 and 1998–1999) demonstrated a clear correlation between mink presence and water vole decline. In research aimed at finding out more about the importance of water vole in the mink diet, 1,345 mink scats were collected from riparian sites in Derbyshire, Leicestershire, Nottinghamshire and Staffordshire where there were still water voles present. Analysis of these scats showed that water vole was the most important prey species making up

Water vole pup looking out for danger from the walls of the Cromford Canal.

32.2 per cent of content in May and June, and featuring most highly in the first half of the year when water vole numbers are at their lowest and the population is most vulnerable.[6]

6) Strachan, C. and Jefferies, D.J., 'An assessment of the diet of the feral American mink Mustela vison from scats collected in areas where water voles Arvicola terrestris occur' in *Naturalist*, Vol.121 (1996), pp73–81. (1996)

AMERICAN MINK IN THE UK

Fur farming became established in England, Wales and Scotland in the late 1940s and 1950s. In the 1960s there were 700 fur farms in the UK. This initially ill-regulated, and what many consider immensely cruel, industry resulted in many escapes in the early years. Mink went on to establish wild populations that have proved catastrophic for the water vole. The first feral mink known to have bred successfully in the wild were found in the River Teign in Devon in 1956. The industry then became regulated so that by 1962 fur farms had to obtain licences and install high-security fencing. The increased costs reduced both the number of farms and escapes, but by now this was a case of shutting the stable door once the horse had bolted. By the early 1960s feral mink were found all across south-west England and south-west Wales.

A government-funded trapping campaign began in England, Wales and Scotland in 1965, but was abandoned in 1970 as the sheer number of mink overwhelmed the resources to deal with the problem. Over a five-year period, the Ministry of Agriculture, Fisheries and Food trapped and killed over 5,000 mink in England and Wales. The Department of Agriculture and Fisheries for Scotland trapped and killed over 2,000 mink. This campaign and many others that have followed it have been very effective locally, but had little effect on the fast-spreading populations of feral mink. The pattern of distribution of mink in the 1970s matched the location of fur farms, which were predominantly in the west and north of Britain. The Game and Wildlife Conservation Trust publish mortality figures in their annual National Gamebag Census. Between 1961 and 1965, 126 mink were caught and despatched. This figure increased to nearly 4,000 between 1981 and 1985 but this is probably a fraction of the true numbers, as not all gamekeepers submit statistics to the census.

Contrary to popular belief, animal rights activists who released mink into the wild in the 1990s are not primarily responsible for the spread of mink throughout Britain, which had occurred much earlier. It is doubtful that those animals released in the 1990s had any impact on feral mink populations, which by then had started to decline at a rapid rate. In 2000, mink farming was banned in Britain and the 11 remaining farms were closed. This trade continues to boom elsewhere in Europe, especially in Poland, and now China dominates this unsavoury trade.

The map shown on page 180 shows the extent to which mink had expanded their range from 1952 to 2012, covering most of mainland Britain with 1,370 occupied ten-kilometre squares. The map on page 181 presents a very different picture with far less dense coverage of just 819 occupied ten-kilometre squares recorded between 2008 and 2012. The national decline in mink numbers, which began in the 1990s, coincided with their expansion into some new areas.

United Kingdom - American Mink presence all records (1952 - 2012)
1,370 occupied 10km grid squares

Hampshire and Isle of Wight Wildlife Trust
Beechcroft House, Vicarage Lane
Curdridge, Hampshire
SO32 2DP

N

180

United Kingdom - American Mink presence (2008 - 2012)
819 occupied 10km grid squares

people's
trust for
endangered
species

Scottish Natural Heritage
All Nàdar na h-Alba

Environment
Agency

Hampshire and Isle of Wight Wildlife Trust
Beechcroft House, Vicarage Lane
Curdridge, Hampshire
SO32 2DP

Map reproduced by Hampshire and Isle of Wight Wildlife Trust (Ordnance Survey licence no. 100015632) with the permission of Her Majesty's Stationery Office, Crown Copyright 2014.
Unauthorised reproduction infringes Copyright and may lead to prosecution or civil proceedings.
Water vole and mink data supplied by Wildlife Trusts and local record centres in England. Used by permission.
Detailed River Network and Catchment Data Supplied by the Environment Agency under licence 2010

Z ◄—

MINK IN DERBYSHIRE

The first mink recorded in Derbyshire were trapped in 1965 by the Ministry of Agriculture, Fisheries and Food; these were found east of Derwent reservoir close to the border with South Yorkshire. While I have been unable to establish where all mink farms were located in the county, I have been told of the existence of one in Two Dales from which mink were released in the 1960s. This location, midway along the county's major river, the Derwent, would have caused catastrophic damage if these animals were able to establish breeding populations. Another mink farm was located in Swanwick near to the River Amber, a tributary of the Derwent.

Up until 1991, just 22 feral mink had been recorded in Derbyshire over a period of 26 years, averaging less than one a year. In 1992, in one year alone, mink were recorded in double figures. At the centre of England, Derbyshire comes at a mid point in the time sequence of the spread of mink from the south and west. Numbers were increasing in the county at a time when a decline was well established in western and south-western regions. There are now records of mink through-out Derbyshire's river systems, including the tributaries and the headwaters of the Derwent, Erewash, Dove, Manifold, Wye, Lathkill, Bradford, Noe and Etherow.

All of Derbyshire's canals have had mink recorded on them.

Derbyshire Wildlife Trust's Water for Wildlife project has been monitoring the presence and absence of otter, water vole and mink in the county since 2000. Over 15 years, surveys revealed a sharp rise in mink presence in 2002, followed by a steady decline then crash in 2010. In a trend that bucks the national picture, records of mink presence have been rising again over the past four years. In 2014, mink presence was recorded in 11 per cent of otter and mink surveys and they are now well established in north-east Derbyshire, where they were formerly scarce.

Note the changing areas of recorded mink presence in the maps that follow. The first map (pre 1997) shows the main concentration of mink records on the Trent and the southern stretches of both the Dove and the Derwent, with a significant number of records further north – especially on the Wye.

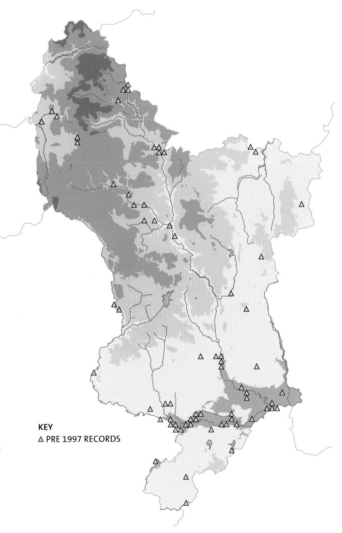

KEY
△ PRE 1997 RECORDS

Maps on this and the facing page show mink presence in Derbyshire according to records held by Derbyshire Wildlife Trust and data supplied by Derbyshire Mammal Group from 1965 to July 2015. To locate major towns and rivers refer to the Derbyshire map on page 70.

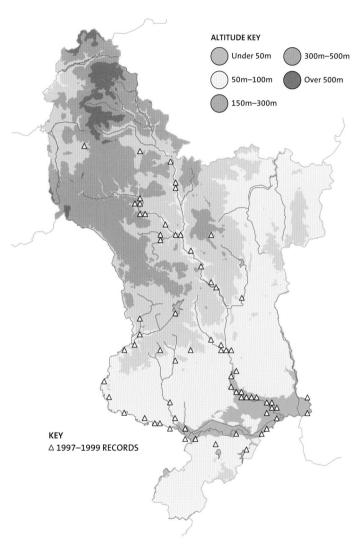

ALTITUDE KEY

Under 50m   300m–500m

50m–100m   Over 500m

150m–300m

KEY
△ 1997–1999 RECORDS

This map shows the expansion of the mink's range all along the Dove (on the western county border) with records spread out along the Derwent and into the Ecclesbourne, the Lathkill and the Wye and fewer records in the Dark Peak (where they were first found).

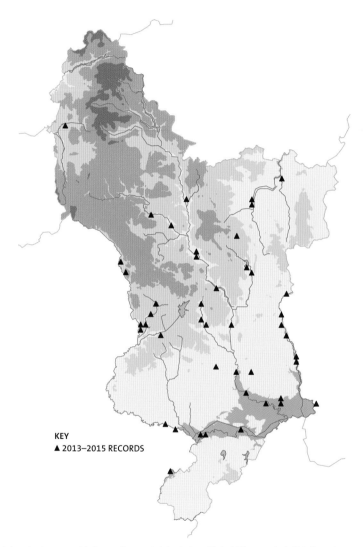

KEY
▲ 2013–2015 RECORDS

This map is based on less survey data than earlier maps but clearly shows that mink have penetrated into the eastern side of the county along the Erewash, the Amber, the Rother and Chesterfield Canal. Trapping efforts by fishing clubs appear to have greatly reduced mink presence along the upper Derwent, the Wye, the Lathkill and the Bradford.

TRAPPING MINK

'For the last 12 years the numbers of water voles have been maintained and in some cases have increased on the Derwent, Wye, Lathkill and Bradford as a direct consequence of us killing mink on specially made raft traps.'
WARREN SLANEY

Ever since they were first detected breeding in the wild in the 1960s, feral mink have been trapped and dispatched by gamekeepers, river keepers, local authorities, government agencies, conservation groups and landowners. However, setting conventional traps is fraught with dangers to other wildlife, so daily checking is a legal requirement to ensure that no animal is trapped for too long. This is very labour intensive. For decades traps were set on land and along waterways, based on both observed field signs for mink and guesswork, but since the 2000s the Game and Wildlife Conservation Trust (GWCT) has researched and developed the use of mink rafts as a means of monitoring for mink and other wildlife. These are trapping devices set on rafts constructed from plywood and polystyrene and secured to riverside trees or shrubs.

The mink raft is a simple and low-tech device used to detect and monitor species. If mink are detected the device is set as a trap, which must be checked early in the morning after the mink's nocturnal activity. The raft design allows for any mammal to enter an enclosed tunnel, which provides a dark space irresistible to the inquisitive mink. Inside the tunnel a layer of damp clay is spread over a block of saturated 'oasis' (as used by flower arrangers) and set into a secured plastic basket. Any visitor to the raft will leave its footprints so that otter, water vole, rat, polecat or mink can be identified. If mink are detected the raft is then set as a trap, either with a spring trap or cage trap (for live capture). Defra-approved spring traps kill instantly at the moment of capture and are considered humane. But there are some risks of killing non-targeted animals with spring traps even when monitoring has taken place, so GWCT recommend the use of the live-capture traps to ensure the release of non-target species. Most wildlife conservation agencies use live-capture traps. Once caught, it is illegal to rerelease mink back into the wild. The method of killing recommended by GWCT is shooting with an air pistol.

As head river keeper for the Haddon Estate, Warren Slaney has extensive experience of trapping and despatching mink:

'An upstream river keeper said to me, "I'd have laid diamonds that I didn't have mink on my river". We put rafts down and straight away we were catching mink. When we started we had two dozen in the first 20 months. The critical area is in the Wye-Derwent confluence. We'll have about three traps around. It's clearer water; fresher smelling and they head for it. If we can catch them before they come up to the Wye that means they can't get up to Cressbrook, the Lathkill or into the Bradford. Mink are not like otters, you don't know they're there. Otters, you know they're there. Everywhere you look there are kills, and spraint. They leave their calling card all over the river. You know when they're there and you know when they're gone. He's a big animal and he's got a lot of impact. The mink's not. It's something that's far more subtle and even though you can be out at dawn on the river you miss them. The moorhens and coots hate them. They really clatter. But you very rarely see them.

'We use the raft system, which works a treat. You can't use the live-trapping system. You can't check every day. So the wetted clay in the raft gives you an indication of what's about. As long as you check every week, if you see the star prints in the clay, you put the trap back in and you'll get it in a couple of days. They've got an absolute weakness for tunnels and islands. So you give them a tunnel and an island and they can't help it, you bypass all their instincts. Just like they can bypass the water voles' security system, we bypass their defences by giving them an island.

'They're the only animals I know that will come to the front of the trap when you appear – they don't go to the back. They come to the front – they want to know who you are. They are almost fearless.

'I can't stand mink. I really hate them. I think you have to if you're going to be a good trapper. They go into a colony and take one water vole a day. The planning, the premeditated murder of that animal, it makes you hate it. They've got so much confidence: "I know I can come back for more. These creatures have got no defence against what I've got and I can come back whenever I want." I don't have any problem shooting mink at all. The water vole has coexisted with all our native predators and the mink has blasted all that advantage away.

'I think we've got way less mink than we had. We had four this year. I was trapping early on in April, that's a good time to get them, when they're moving around. We definitely notice small ones at the back-end of the year, lots of small males in October and November. We run our mink traps through until the first floods at the end of November. I've just made up a dozen new rafts.'

Mink trapping is said to be most effective in late summer or autumn when young mink are dispersing, or in the spring before kits are born. But to really support the recovery of water vole populations, mink control must go hand in hand with habitat improvement.

TOP: A mink raft secured to a tree at the confluence of the Wye and the Derwent.
BOTTOM: Mink caught in a live capture trap that had been placed inside a mink raft.
Photo: Derbyshire Wildlife Trust.

POLECATS: A CASE OF MISTAKEN IDENTITY

'Foumart, filimart, fitchet' – local names
for the polecat.

In the way that water voles can be mistaken for rats, so can polecats (*Mustela putorius*) be mistaken for mink. Polecats are native mustelids similar in size to mink with long sinuous bodies and they leave almost identical footprints, scats and feeding signs. The polecat can be distinguished from the mink by its strong facial mask with white ear margins. These beautiful animals are protected under Schedule 6 of the Wildlife and Countryside Act of 1981 and are a UK priority Biodiversity Action Plan species. Once extinct, the polecat has returned to Derbyshire where it is vital that those responsible for trapping know the difference between these two species.

The polecat was, according to Jourdain, 'formerly very common and widely distributed' in Derbyshire but he notes in 1905, 'it is practically extinct in the south and occurs rarely in the north and west'. The last record was at Bradley near Ashbourne: 'in the spring of 1900 one was trapped, but managed to escape, although it left a foot in the trap.'[7]

After the total extinction of the polecat in England and Scotland, a remnant Welsh population began to expand in the 1960s and in the late 1980s and 1990 came the first recent reports of polecats in Derbyshire. The native polecat breeds freely with feral ferrets to produce the hybrid polecat-ferret. *The Mammals of Derbyshire* (2012) has over 200 records of polecats of which nearly two thirds were confirmed as true polecat and the rest hybrid. The majority of these records are from animals killed on the road and 'probably under-represent the real status of the species in the county'.

Mammalogist Johnny Birks has been studying, recording and writing about the polecat and other mustelids for decades. In his most recent book, *Polecats*, he draws attention to the dangers of inadvertently trapping and killing this protected species by the use of spring traps:

'Some of the target pest species listed are much the same size as polecats so, for example, a spring trap set on the ground to kill rabbits, mink or grey squirrels will inevitably pose a risk to polecats. It follows that many spring traps are deployed in ways that make it inevitable that polecats are sometimes killed or injured.

'It is difficult to estimate the numbers of polecats injured or killed by spring trapping because trappers are unlikely to divulge such occurrences because of concerns about legal consequences … on welfare grounds alone there is a strong case for amending current practice to allow only those methods that do not harm non-target species.'[8]

Polecats feed principally on rabbits in the summer and on rats in the winter – often moving into farmyards. On moorland or riparian habitats they are particularly vulnerable to trapping, so well managed cage traps are the obvious solution:

'Polecats also enter cage traps set for mink, for example, even including those set on floating 'mink rafts' as part of wide scale mink control operations. Provided that all traps are checked first thing every morning, and that trappers can readily identify polecats and release them as swiftly as possible, there should be little harm arising from such accidental captures.'

---

7) Jourdain, in Page, ed., *The Victoria History of the County of Derby* (London, 1905).   8) Birks, *Polecats (British Natural History Series)* (London, 2016).

Polecat (*Mustela putorius*) photographed at the Chestnut Centre.

MINK ERADICATION: THE SCOTTISH MINK INITIATIVE

The Scottish Mink Initiative aims to protect native wildlife including the water vole and ground-nesting birds by wiping out mink across vast tracts of land. Initially, researchers from the University of Aberdeen led a four-year project to systematically remove mink from an entire river catchment. Mink were cleared from the Ythan catchment area in Aberdeenshire, demonstrating that it is possible to eliminate mink across river systems. This project expanded to become the Scottish Mink Initiative, which aims to secure multiple adjacent river catchments in the hope 'that the continued success of the project could eventually lead to the eradication of mink across the entire north-east of Scotland'.

Community engagement has been a key to the success of this project, with hundreds of volunteers working with academics, conservationists, project officers and fisheries in a partnership involved in reporting, catching and dispatching mink in 'the largest invasive non-native species eradication project worldwide'. The ambition, community support and success of this project is without precedent. Water voles have recolonised many areas in a brief space of time. A look at any map of Scotland gives an idea of the scale of this achievement: 'Initially the Scottish Mink Initiative area was to cover ~ 20,000 km² from north Tayside, across Aberdeenshire, Moray, the Cairngorms and the Highlands, however the work area was expanded during Phase 1 (into the north-west) and the actual area covered was ~ 28,500 km². Our southerly boundary runs from Lunan Bay to Forfar to Coupar Angus to Dunkeld to Aberfeldy and finally out to Loch Rannoch.'[9]

However, it is doubtful that such an approach could succeed in densely populated areas of Britain where the plight of our native wildlife and the damage caused by mink is often poorly understood. Several river bailiffs and countryside rangers have told me how mink rafts are routinely vandalised by visitors to the countryside who regard any 'gamekeepery' equipment as a legitimate target for attack.

A list of organisations with advice on mink control and habitat restoration is given on page 235.

---

9) *Scottish Mink Initiative* [online] <http://www.scottishmink.org.uk/about-us>

Rannoch Moor at the southern end of the Scottish Mink Initiative's area for catchment-wide mink eradication.

The disappearing water vole

Alarm at the rate at which mink were spreading and the impact this was apparently having on the water vole population of Britain led to the first national survey of water vole and mink in 1989–1990, conducted and studied by Rob Strachan and Don Jefferies for the Vincent Wildlife Trust. The field survey was carried out entirely by Rob Strachan, 'living and travelling around Britain in a camper van'.

Around a third of the sites chosen had historical records of water vole presence and the other two thirds were selected from representative watercourses found in an evenly spread selection of ten-kilometre squares covering the whole of mainland Britain. These are referred to as 'baseline sites' in what follows. An outline of the scope and methods used in the two national water vole and mink surveys are found in appendix 2 on page 234.

'Despite the daunting task of visiting nearly three thousand sites, it had been anticipated that a single surveyor could apply constant effort throughout, allowing for even coverage, particularly in areas supporting few or no water voles … Searching for water voles between Lands End and John O'Groats, I was able to find the species where they had been overlooked before, such as among the streams and mires of Rannoch Moor or the Flow Country of Caithness and Sutherland.' Strachan, *Water Voles (British Natural History Series)* (London, 1997).

Results of the first survey were grouped according to regions based on water authority areas (demonstrating how whole catchments are affected by the expansion or loss of species) and were analysed and published in 1993. The survey found that water voles were present in nearly 48 per cent of sites across all regions of mainland Britain, with a higher presence recorded in historical sites.

Severn Trent region, which covers all of Derbyshire, had a high positive record at this stage, with water voles recorded in nearly 35 per cent of the 192 baseline sites and over 75 per cent in the 85 historical sites. Nearly half (47.74 per cent) of the sites surveyed in the Severn Trent region had water voles in 1990. The population of water voles in mainland Britain was then estimated to be 7,294,000.

Mink presence was found in nearly 35 per cent of survey sites, with an estimated pre-breeding adult mink population in mainland Britain of 105,650.

United Kingdom - Water Vole presence all records (1861 - 2012)
1,482 occupied 10km grid squares

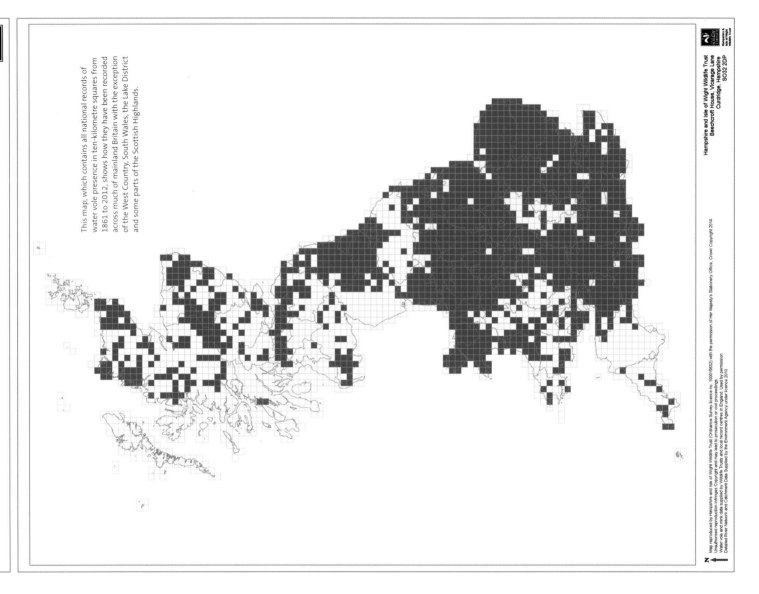

This map, which contains all national records of water vole presence in ten-kilometre squares from 1861 to 2012, shows how they have been recorded across much of mainland Britain with the exception of the West Country, South Wales, the Lake District and some parts of the Scottish Highlands.

Hampshire and Isle of Wight Wildlife Trust
Beechcroft House, Vicarage Lane
Curdridge, Hampshire
SO32 2DP

Map reproduced by Hampshire and Isle of Wight Wildlife Trust (Ordnance Survey licence no. 100015632) with the permission of Her Majesty's Stationery Office. Crown Copyright 2014.
Unauthorised reproduction infringes Copyright and may lead to prosecution or civil proceedings.
Water vole and mink data supplied by Wildlife Trusts and local record centres in England. Used by permission.
Detailed River Network and Catchment Data Supplied by the Environment Agency under licence 2010

N

United Kingdom - Water Vole presence (2008 - 2012)
689 occupied 10km grid squares

This map graphically illustrates how the water vole's presence across mainland Britain has been devastated with many localised extinctions.

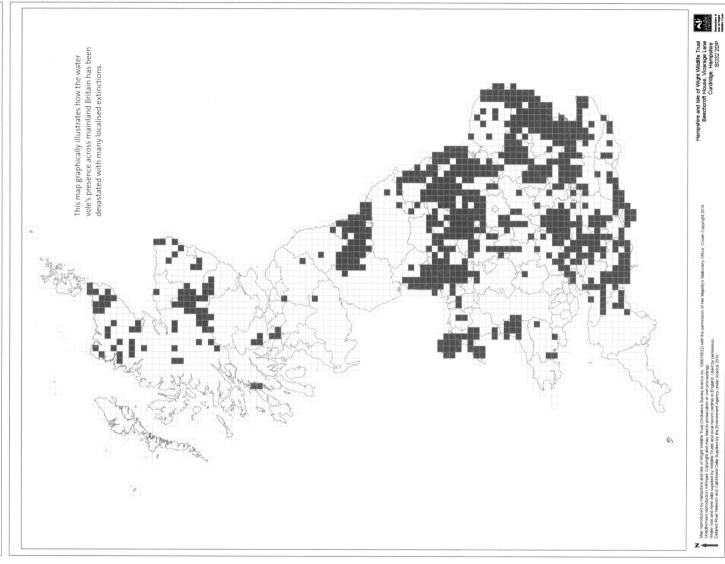

Hampshire and Isle of Wight Wildlife Trust
Beechcroft House, Vicarage Lane
Curdridge, Hampshire
SO32 2DP

CATASTROPHIC LOSSES

Seven years later, the follow-up national survey measured changes in population, range and densities of water vole and mink. The same 3,000 sites were surveyed between 1996 and 1998. Surveyors and researchers discovered catastrophic losses. There were signs of water voles in just 216 of the 1,970 baseline sites where just seven years before there had been well over 700. The overall loss of occupied sites was 69.62 per cent.

The actual decline was greater than that, as the numbers of water voles had decreased in the remaining occupied sites. Jefferies and Strachan estimated that the total summer population of water voles in England, Scotland and Wales recorded from 1996 to 1998 was 875,000: 'an overall loss of 6,419,000 or 80% in only seven years.'

The findings of these two surveys in the 1990s became the basis for targeted research and conservation priorities over the next 25 years.

CHANGING WATER VOLE BEHAVIOUR

A study by Jeppsson of water voles in Sweden defined four kinds of water vole habitat as 'optimal' (important breeding area), 'secondary' (with some breeding), 'marginal' (where water voles survive but don't breed), and 'transient' (where water voles pass through or survive for a short time).

A study of water voles in four rivers in North Yorkshire by Woodroffe et al. in 1988 classified sites as either 'core' or 'peripheral'. The core breeding sites had latrines and other signs of occupation whereas the peripheral sites had just scattered droppings and feeding signs. In the past, researchers had concluded that peripheral sites were those occupied by non-breeding juveniles or by water voles in transit – on the move before locating to new territory.

In this survey, researchers found that the water voles in the peripheral sites exhibited 'nervous behaviour' and were impossible to catch in the tunnel-like water vole traps. A higher percentage of the voles in peripheral sites were observed out in the open, which may have indicated a reluctance to stay underground in burrows.

TOP: A water vole sits on garden waste (leylandii) thrown into the Cromford Canal.
BOTTOM: Water vole peering out of its burrow entrance on the Derwent.

The second national water vole and mink survey (1996–1998) found that peripheral sites were present all through the year, including during the most territorial periods for water voles. This indicates that some sites were occupied by adult water voles not engaged in any territorial breeding behaviour. They found a strong correlation between peripheral sites and impending loss of occupation and concluded that 'it is likely that these no-latrine sites … may be just a transient stage in the degradation of a water vole 'core' breeding site into one with water voles absent.'

The first national water vole survey found that all 1,418 occupied sites had burrows. Seven years later in almost a fifth of the remaining 400 occupied sites there were no evident burrows. The 'nervous behaviour' observed in North Yorkshire and evidence of a reduction in burrow use by water voles indicates that new behaviours had developed over a very brief period of unprecedented and rapacious predation by mink. These small rodents had learned in a very short time that burrows are unsafe, and that what was formerly a refuge had become a trap. A great deal of conservation effort is now going into the development of reedbeds as more secure habitat for water voles.

I have looked for water voles in many different Derbyshire locations and on several sites found the animals or signs of their presence, such as food remains and scattered droppings, but no evidence of latrines. These are rather ominous signs.

DECLINING MINK

The national water vole and mink surveys found that mink occupation of sites monitored had declined by almost a third between 1990 and 1997. The extent of the decline varied immensely in the different regions. In the north-west of England nearly 95 per cent of mink-occupied sites had declined. In some parts of Britain, mainly the south-east and East Anglia, mink numbers were still increasing in the early 1990s following on from the late expansion of mink into those areas in a case of last in, last out. The spread of mink and the pattern of their decline came from the west. What also came from the west and helped to drive the mink on and out was the welcome return of the native otter.

'The timing and extent of the decline could be clearly linked to the timing and size of the recovering otter population.'[10]

---

10) Jefferies, Strachan and Strachan, 'The expansion and decline of the mink population in Britain' in Jeffries, ed., *The Water Vole and Mink Survey of Britain 1996–1998 with a history of the long-term changes in the status of both species and their causes* (Ledbury, 2003).

WATER VOLE DECLINE IN DERBYSHIRE

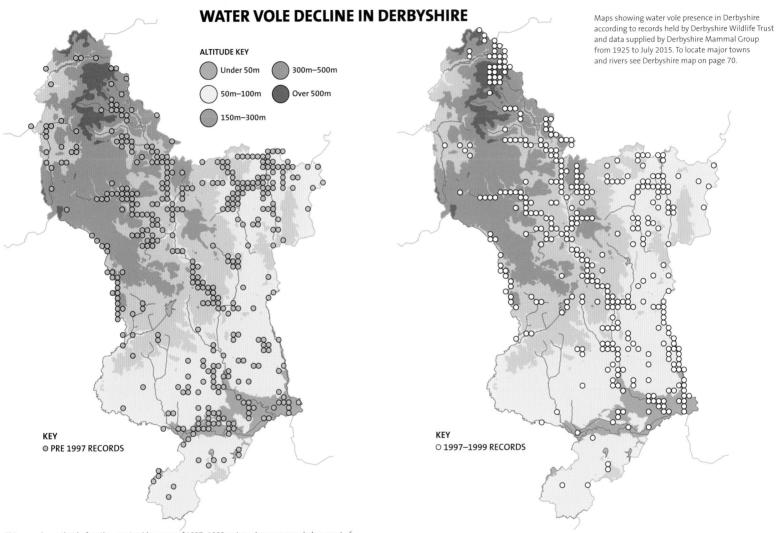

ALTITUDE KEY

- Under 50m
- 50m–100m
- 150m–300m
- 300m–500m
- Over 500m

Maps showing water vole presence in Derbyshire according to records held by Derbyshire Wildlife Trust and data supplied by Derbyshire Mammal Group from 1925 to July 2015. To locate major towns and rivers see Derbyshire map on page 70.

KEY
◉ PRE 1997 RECORDS

KEY
○ 1997–1999 RECORDS

This map shows that before the countywide survey of 1997–1999 water voles were recorded on most of Derbyshire's canals and major rivers including the Trent, the Dove, the Wye, the Rother, much of the Derwent and the Goyt in the north-west. While some records date back to 1925 there are very few prior to 1969 and no systematic recording took place until 1997.

This map, which reflects data from the first (and only) countywide survey of 1997–1999, shows few records in the south-west of the county and an increase in records in both the south-east (along the Erewash) with a strong cluster of records in the headwaters of the Derwent, high up in the Dark Peak – both recording new survey data.

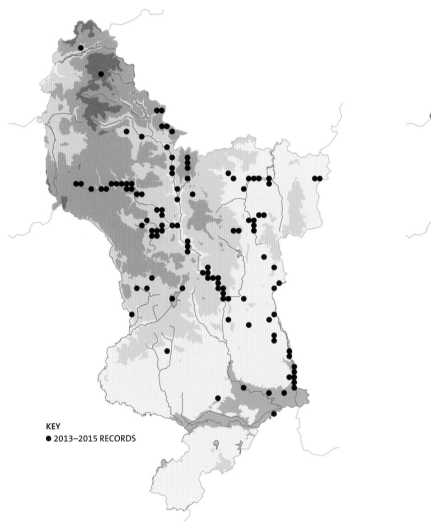

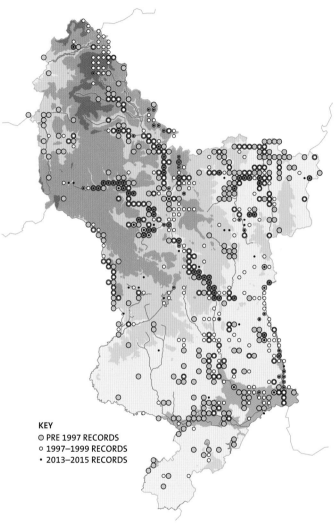

KEY
● 2013–2015 RECORDS

KEY
◉ PRE 1997 RECORDS
○ 1997–1999 RECORDS
· 2013–2015 RECORDS

This map is based on incomplete records from 2013–2015, but the sparse scattering of positive records does reflect a genuine pattern of losses in the county and should be compared with the maps showing changing patterns of mink presence in Derbyshire on pages 182 and 183.

This map shows the history of losses and a few gains where water voles may not have been surveyed before. The dots with two rings and a black core represent the persistence of water voles in historic sites that have supported water voles over several decades.

OTTER AND MINK

There is a high level of competition and antagonism between the species, and as otters weigh up to ten times the weight of an adult mink this is clearly an unequal contest. Both animals have linear ranges along watercourses so they are highly likely to encounter each other. The national water vole and mink surveys demonstrated a clear correlation between the advance of the otter and a retreat of mink.

A reintroduction of otters into the upper Thames catchment in 1999 made it possible to measure the impact of otters on a population of mink. Upon the release of 11 female and 7 male otters, mink dramatically declined close to the release sites. After a year, mink occupation was reduced from 77 per cent of sites to 23 per cent. Later monitoring showed that after two years, when the otters were reduced in number and had spread out further through the catchment, there was a continued suppression of mink, but not on the scale seen soon after the release. Mink had become scarcer and their population more fragmented, losing much of their range in the upper Thames.[11]

When otters recolonise naturally, mink decline more slowly, but the fact that they do decline both in density and distribution must be good news for water voles and other riparian wildlife.

There are stories – mainly from fishermen – of otters fighting and killing mink, and mink hair has been found in otter spraints in Russia. Strachan and Jefferies suggest that while there are large numbers of mink and relatively few otters occupying the same area, the otters appear to exhibit a kind of 'mink rage' while larger populations of otters seem to coexist with mink:

'The highest mink loss is suffered when a medium-sized otter population interacts with a large mink population ... The mechanism bringing about the actual decline of the mink would appear to be increasing interference with its survival efficiency and finally lethal fighting between these two mustelids of unequal size and weight.'[12]

11) Bonesi and Macdonald, 'Impact of released Eurasian otters on a population of American mink: a test using an experimental approach' in *Oikos*, Vol.106, No.1 (July 2004).   12) Jefferies, 'Interactions between the Three Riparian Species', in Jefferies, ed., *The water vole and mink survey of Britain 1996–1998*.

TOP: Mink. BOTTOM: Otter.

The concerted efforts of gamekeepers, river keepers, fishing clubs, local authorities and conservation bodies to capture and kill mink have had a positive effect on local populations of water voles and other species predated by mink. However the return of the otter could have the greatest impact of all in reestablishing some balance to the wildlife of waterways. Mink are generalists so they can exploit many other food sources away from the rivers, and as opportunists they can return when the 'coast is clear' of otters. There are concerns that once driven from the major rivers of Derbyshire, mink may further seek out more remote territory in the uplands to exploit small, vulnerable populations of water voles but, so far, their incursions appear to be limited. No one predicts that otters will wipe out mink and halt the ongoing devastation of Britain's water voles. However, there is cause for some hope as the research on the upper Thames catchment has made it possible to make some predictions on how many otters are needed to put mink under sufficient pressure to allow the recovery of the water vole.

'Our evidence suggests that the European otter will not eliminate the American mink, but that otters are able to reduce mink density to about half of the density that they are able to attain in their absence … Importantly, otters also induce a fragmentation in mink populations.'

Bonesi and Macdonald conclude, 'It is now a matter of establishing whether the fragmentation of mink distribution will be high enough and mink densities will be low enough to allow the co-existence of mink and water voles.'

part 7

The Future for Water Voles

The future for water voles

The human population of the United Kingdom is just over 64 million (2013). The population of field voles, our most common mammal, is around 75 million.[1] In the distant past, Britain's most common mammal was the water vole, which far exceeded the number of field voles. If relative numbers persisted today, even with the disappearance of most of our wild places, a current population of water voles might number 100 million. As it is, the water vole is our fastest declining mammal with a pre-breeding spring population of far less than one million.

The decline of the water vole has a long history but has accelerated to such an extent that it appears to be heading towards extinction. In this book much has been said about mink and its role in the misfortunes of the water vole, but the story is really about what we humans have done to our environment by squeezing wild creatures to the very brink through lost and damaged habitat.

Since the Second World War, agricultural intensification and urban development have led to the loss of floodplain habitat. Wetlands have declined both locally and nationally as a result of drainage for building or agriculture.

Our rivers and streams have been straightened, canalised and contained by concrete and steel structures. To keep many of our unnatural watercourses sound, engineering and maintenance work including flood defences, bank protection, de-silting and dredging operations have to be undertaken on a regular basis. This necessary work often causes temporary or permanent damage to water voles' habitat. Waterside vegetation in public and private spaces is often insensitively managed, and overzealous mowing or strimming removes both food and cover for water voles and other species. The water vole has the highest level of legal protection given to mammals in the UK, but human projects continue to encroach on the shrinking world of this small rodent.

1) This estimate of the pre-breeding population of field voles appears in Lambin, 'Field vole Microtus agrestis, Rodents: Order Rodentia' in Harris and Yalden, eds., *The Mammals of the British Isles* (Southampton, 2008).

OPPOSITE PAGE: Water vole in April.

Planning, development and mitigation

Local planning authorities must now scrutinise any construction work or modification of watercourses, or change of land use where water voles are present. Disturbance or destruction of the water vole or its habitat has become a criminal offence so, where possible, new developments should be located away from areas where there are or may be water voles. Water vole colonies use habitat differently at different times of the year, and a survey may just record temporary absence, so this should be taken into consideration.

In Derbyshire, and in many other counties, the Wildlife Trust holds the data on water voles and must be consulted about their presence. If water voles are present and a development poses any kind of threat to them and their habitat, then considerable steps must be taken to mitigate any potential damage at the planning stage. *The Water Vole Conservation Handbook*, written by Rob Strachan and published by the Wildlife Conservation Research Unit, is the water vole conservation bible and is now in its third edition (2011) and a fourth edition is underway. The handbook is based on decades of research and conservation practice and deals with every conceivable issue to do with surveys, habitat management, development and mitigation. Many planning scenarios with their attendant problems and conflicts are outlined together with solutions and numerous examples of best practice.

Mitigation aims to avoid any negative impact on the animal and its habitat. This can involve anything from the restoring or creating of new habitat, moving water voles and then returning them once work is completed, moving them altogether to a new site, or even introducing captive-bred animals. However, any loss of habitat caused by development reduces the possibilities of future colonisation, and may fragment populations so that they become unviable. In an ideal world, planning decisions should be made not looking at the tiny and threatened water vole population of today, but by making allowances for a brighter future, so that new developments do not prevent recovering populations from being able to inhabit areas where the species once thrived.

A development such as HS2 could alter the hydrology of adjacent wetlands well beyond its immense planned footprint, and just how effective water voles' legal protection is once the bulldozers get moving is anyone's guess.

MOVING WATER VOLES

Animals know where they want to be, so moving them from their chosen homes to avoid potential hazards caused by building or maintenance work is fraught with problems. In the past, water voles have been moved on by using a 'displacement technique', which involves persuading them to move along to adjacent habitat by removing all vegetation and strimming down to bare earth thereby making the existing habitat untenable for them. But there are numerous problems with this approach, as on several sites water voles have shown that they are very attached to their patch and return to their damaged home range, which can result in animals starving or being left in the open to be predated. This practice is currently under review. Derek Gow is an ecological consultant specialising in water vole conservation through mitigation, translocation and captive reproduction. He believes that displacement is ineffective:

'They do not displace easily and will readily attempt to return to their original territory. Often the only alternative may be to trap and remove them outside their breeding season and there is significant evidence that this process can work well. They must be released back into environments which offer good food and cover and these landscapes take time to establish.'[2]

Needless to say, the highly specialised work involved in mitigation measures involves skilled, licensed and experienced people to carry them out. All of these approaches incur risk to the animals and to the populations in the area, no matter how carefully they are undertaken.

Water voles captured both in and on a Pringles tube.
Photos: Derek Gow Consultancy Ltd.

2) Derek Gow Consultancy Ltd, *Water Vole Development mitigation* [online] <http://www.watervoles.com/water%20vole%20development%20mitigation.htm> accessed 2015.

'Water vole restoration utilising either translocated animals or captive bred offspring has become an identified component of the national Biodiversity Action Plan for this species. Water vole translocations (the direct movement of wild caught animals from one site to another) – which have commonly been practised as a component of human development projects – are problematic due to the low number of animals frequently involved, their high territorial fidelity (Dean, 2003) and their short reproductive lifespan. The sourcing of sufficient offspring from healthy donor populations (harvesting) might be a mechanism for providing future release stocks but this – as yet unquantified – process can only be employed if the security of donor populations can be guaranteed.'

Over ten years, Derek's company has bred more than 10,000 water voles or provided temporary lodging for them when their homes were disrupted by development. The 'farming' of water voles is a delicate business of animal husbandry that involves maintaining genetic diversity by adding new bloodlines so that, 'you end up with a stock that is vibrant and vigorous by adding more to the stockpot'.[3] However the *Water Vole Conservation Handbook* recommends that populations are never translocated between Scotland and England/Wales, 'to ensure that lineages are not mixed and evolutionary heritage lost'. It further recommends a restriction in distance that populations are moved, and that the lineage of individual water voles can be traced to their landscape of origin.

Derek believes that, 'no clear information exists regarding any clear line of introgression between the two forms and over time their practical retention as separate entities – if indeed they ever were – may well prove impractical.'

Derek has been involved with over 30 successful water vole reintroduction programmes in many locations across Britain.

Rebecca Northey handling a water vole.
Photo: Derek Gow Consultancy Ltd.

3) Gow, 'Water vole reintroduction projects – the lessons and the success factors' in *ECOS* Vol.28(1) [online] <http://www.watervoles.com/index_htm_files/Water%20vole%20reintroduction%20projects.pdf>

Reintroduction programmes

'Habitat creation and restoration projects are hugely valuable for most wildlife. There are some species for which introduction programmes are necessary simply because populations have become so fragmented and the species is not very mobile. The Environment Agency has created nearly 5,000 hectares of wetland and river habitats in the last ten years, and worked hard to tackle unsustainable abstraction from our rivers, to the extent that some 55 billion litres of water each year is now returned to the environment. However we are keen to support carefully located water vole release projects as well, but only as long as there is rigorous control of American mink in the catchment. This is essential if the populations of water voles are to benefit from these healthier rivers and new habitats.'[4] Alastair Driver, the Environment Agency's national conservation manager and chair of the UK Water Vole Steering Group.

Following a successful water vole reintroduction programme in the Bude river catchment in Cornwall in 2013, there are now breeding colonies in every county in England. The once common water vole had become extinct in Cornwall in 1989 and the closest populations in East Devon were too distant for natural recolonisation through dispersal. The release of captive-bred animals was organised by the Environment Agency together with a local wildlife charity Westland Countryside Stewards. Reintroductions have occurred in various locations where there is good habitat but no chance of natural colonisation through dispersal. There are discussions underway on the possibility of reintroduction into the River Dove catchment in Derbyshire but such a move cannot be countenanced while mink are so far from being controlled.

---

4) Environment Agency press release (27 August 2014) [online] <https://www.gov.uk/government/news/water-voles-return-to-every-county-in-england>

Water quality

Our rivers are the cleanest they have been for three decades and the return of the top predator, the otter, is testament to the returning biodiversity of our river systems. For this we have to thank the European Union and the Environment Agency. The EU set out to protect and improve water quality by adopting the Water Framework Directive in 2000. The directive has established a framework for the protection of inland surface waters (rivers and lakes), transitional waters (estuaries), coastal waters and groundwater. All member states established 'river basin districts' that include inland and coastal waters falling within defined areas linked by river catchments.

Most of Derbyshire's river catchments are within the Humber River Basin District. The Water Framework Directive requires that all waters must reach at least 'good status' by 2015, or if this cannot be achieved then new or less stringent targets can be set for 2021 or 2027. The status refers to an overall status with both an ecological and chemical component and a scale that is graded high, good, moderate, poor or bad. These are the components that are measured in order to ascertain the status of a water body:

• Physico-chemical, for example, nutrients, pH, dissolved oxygen, ammonia.

• Biological elements, for example, phytoplankton, macroalgae, fish, invertebrates.

• Specific pollutants, for example, metals and their compounds, organic compounds.

• Hydromorphology, for example, depth, width, flow, structure.[5]

Chemical status is measured either as 'good' or 'fail'.

Rivers within the Peak District National Park are rated among the best in Britain in terms of water quality. However, as much of the land in lowland Derbyshire and within the Peak District National Park is farmland, intensive agricultural practices can threaten river water quality through 'land erosion/ river bed siltation, nutrient enrichment caused by farm yard run off (silage/slurry), heavy applications of fertilisers and slurry'.[6]

5) Environment Agency, 'Figure 2' in *River Basin Management Plan, Humber River Basin District* (December 2009), p14.   6) Peak District National Park Authority, 'River Quality' on *Peak District State of the Park Report* (2013) [online] <http://www.peakdistrict.gov.uk/microsites/sopr/landscape/river-quality>

OPPOSITE PAGE, TOP LEFT: Dipper. TOP RIGHT: Baby coots. BOTTOM LEFT: Grey wagtail. BOTTOM RIGHT: Female goosander.

Catchment Sensitive Farming and Countryside Stewardship

The Catchment Sensitive Farming (CSF) project run by Natural England in partnership with the Environment Agency and Defra, aims to improve water quality in priority catchments in designated areas in England. This scheme to 'improve the environmental performance of farms' gives farmers the opportunity to apply for capital for works to reduce diffuse water pollution caused by agricultural activity. It has now been integrated into the new Countryside Steward-ship agreements and could be at risk of reduced engagement and uptake as financial pressures mount, particularly in the dairy sector, and advisory and monitoring resources become more stretched.

We have come a long way since the River Doe Lea was regarded as the dirtiest river in Europe but many of Derbyshire's rivers are not at 'good status' as required by the Water Framework Directive. It is likely though that some of our rivers are in the healthiest state that they have been since Izaak Walton and Charles Cotton waxed lyrical on their qualities in the 17th century. But what continues to damage our rivers and their ecosystems, proving catastrophic for the water vole and many other species, is the invading aliens.

Invader species

'All the time now we're trying to limit the damage caused by man; invasive animals, invasive plants, pollution and poor land-use.'

WARREN SLANEY

SIGNAL CRAYFISH

White-clawed crayfish (*Austropotamobius pallipes*) is the UK's only native crayfish and its largest freshwater invertebrate; it is also a species of global conservation concern and classified as 'endangered' by the International Union for Conservation of Nature. White-clawed crayfish were once common and widespread but are now rare, as their numbers have been devastated by the introduction of the North American signal crayfish (*Pacifastacus leniusculus*) which is larger than the native crayfish, more aggressive and breeds faster. Critically, the signal crayfish has brought with it a virulent plague that has wiped out the native crayfish in many parts of England. The plague can be spread by water, fishing equipment or boots that have been in contaminated water. Other animals may also spread the spores of the plague, for example, on the feet of birds flying from one water body to another.

During the 1980s the Ministry of Agriculture, Fisheries and Food (MAFF) encouraged farmers to diversify, because many in the industry faced financial ruin due to fixed quotas and cuts in grants. Many smaller operators were particularly badly hit and were persuaded to seek other ways to generate income. MAFF thought that crayfish farming for the catering industry was a good idea and distributed imported American signal crayfish to anyone who cared to have a go at this new venture. Warren Slaney is a man at war with the signal crayfish, spending many hours trapping in an effort to rid the Wye, the Derwent, the Lathkill and the Bradford of these immensely destructive creatures. This is the story as told by Warren, of how the American signal crayfish got into the best fly fishing rivers in Derbyshire that are also home to the otter and water vole:

'In the early 1990s a trio of crayfish (three animals), within a cardboard box, was delivered under the MAFF farming diversification initiative by Royal Mail to a farm in Buxton. They were placed in a pond, which fed directly to the River Wye. During the weeks that followed, the entire population of native white-clawed crayfish was killed in the River Wye by crayfish plague carried by the introduced signal crayfish. The source of the disease was confirmed by the National Rivers Authority (NRA). The UK government and its agencies are directly responsible for the import and spread of the plague to the rivers Wye, the Derwent and their tributaries, and the consequent death of its entire population of native white-clawed crayfish.'

Warren believes that if left unchecked, the signal crayfish could jeopardise the health of the rivers by destroying the rivers' insects and thus the whole ecosystem. Over the past two years signal crayfish have been trapped from the Derwent in huge numbers by local fishing clubs and estates, leading to an increase in river insects and the maintenance of populations of wild trout. Water voles have been known to drown in crayfish traps and licences for trapping are issued by the Environment Agency, which authorises methods that use 'best practice' with consideration for water voles. Trapping on the Derwent has been proved safe for water voles through the use of specially designed traps.

OPPOSITE PAGE: Warren Slaney, head river keeper for the Haddon Estate, with the day's catch of North American signal crayfish.

HIMALAYAN BALSAM

Himalayan balsam (*Impatiens glandulifera*) was introduced into Britain in the 19th century as an ornamental plant. It has since successfully colonised riverbanks, roadsides, damp woodland and waste ground and is now one of Britain's most widespread invasive weeds and present in most river catchments. Standing at between two and three metres tall, it robs native plant species of space, light, nutrients and pollinators, and thereby has a major impact on biodiversity. Himalayan balsam is an annual plant that dies down completely in winter, leaving bare ground with no cover for wildlife and ground that is susceptible to erosion.

The use of herbicides along watercourses presents numerous hazards and must involve consents from the Environment Agency. Manually pulling the plants out involves the least environmental damage but is very time-consuming and can be problematic in inaccessible areas, and the plant also recolonises very quickly. Balsam seeds shoot off in all directions and rapidly take over areas with a blanket coverage that excludes the complex layering of riparian plants that is so important as food source and cover for water voles and other species that live in and by the water. Land managers across the county are trying to deal with the problem of tackling Himalayan balsam to allow the recovery of native species, and locally teams of volunteers organised by Derbyshire Wildlife Trust regularly undertake the heroic task of pulling balsam from riverbanks.

Volunteers for Derbyshire Wildlife Trust removing Himalayan balsam. Photo: Derbyshire Wildlife Trust.

Current research is exploring the option of biological control by employing pathogens that limit the spread of the plant in its native situation. Trials are underway on a 'rust fungus' which has been safety tested in a quarantine laboratory and may be used in future to control the spread of this rampaging alien plant while 'leaving indigenous species intact, so that the ecosystems can be restored'. In July 2014, Defra approved the release of 'the first fungal biological control agent to be released against a weed in the European Union'.[7] The trials were extended in 2015 and once released further it may take five to ten years before Himalayan balsam can be controlled effectively.

7) CABI, *Himalayan balsam release update* [online] <http://himalayanbalsam.cabi.org/release-update>

Custodians of the rivers

'We think we have as many fine rivers, rivulets, and brooks, as any country whatever; and they are all full of trouts, and some of them the best, it is said, by many degrees in England.' (Charles Cotton in *The Compleat Angler*, Part II)

The trout streams and rivers of Derbyshire made famous by Izaak Walton and Charles Cotton are now fished by many clubs, each responsible for their stretch of riverbank and the health of their bit of the river. Fishing clubs and estates and their river keepers and bailiffs are the people now working hardest at limiting the damage done by alien species and the consequent loss of biodiversity.

Warren Slaney believes that there are no easy ways to fix the problems in our rivers:

'In the long summer days, the labourers used to start work at five o'clock in the morning and finish at nine at night because they'd got the light. But also because it was necessary to be out there working to get ahead of nature in order to survive. In order for us to control balsam on the banks of the Derwent and every tributary and all the woods around that are infested we need to start early and finish late. The Derwent doesn't recruit fish well. They don't spawn in it, so the adults like to shoot up side-streams. So we have to try and make the side-streams clean and that means we have to fence them off. Our wild trout fishery ethos means that you have to make the rivers right for wild trout, which also makes them right for everything else.

River Wye at Topley Pike.

'In order to make sure that the eggs don't get covered in silt, you have to reduce the amount of erosion on the banks so you don't get block failure. In order to get good wild trout in the river, for the river's sake we're trying all the time to reduce the impact of the hand of man.'

The continuing presence of water voles in Peak District rivers depends on the trapping efforts of the fishing community, as it is only the fishing clubs and estates that have taken on the job of mink control north of Matlock and through the Peak District National Park. But it is the much larger project of habitat restoration that Warren and other fisheries are engaged in that gives some hope for the future of all the wild creatures of the rivers.

'We're trying to persuade water voles to come and breed, and stay and like it here. I suppose the ideal scenario is, you only see water voles occasionally because there's so much cover for them and you only get the plop when you walk past. The fringe should overhang the river so they're in there hiding. That's what we're after. It suits our wild trout policy. If we were stocking fish it wouldn't matter. But what we're doing is growing trout, getting trout to breed, getting those babies to stay, getting the yearlings to like it here and the big fish to stay. And we're looking after all those elements of the life cycle of the trout and that benefits all the other species as well.'

National status of the water vole

As part of the UK Biodiversity Action Plan process, a revised water vole 'Species Action Plan' was published in 2006 and set out a range of targets to be achieved within a certain timeline. At that time water voles occupied 730 ten-kilometre squares in the UK, and the aim was to retain that range and to increase the numbers of newly occupied squares by another 50 in 2010 – the United Nations International Year of Biodiversity. Further targets were set at five-year intervals up until 2030. By 2008 most of the targets set for 2010 had already been achieved and all signs indicated that populations were making a comeback with animals present in 874 ten-kilometre squares.

Since then, however, statistics released by the Environment Agency and the Wildlife Trusts in 2013 showed that the populations could have fallen by as much as a fifth since 2011. Populations in the south-west, the Lake District and parts of the Midlands were said to be especially vulnerable. However, it was also noted that in some areas the decline may reflect a decline in recorder effort, and funding for water vole surveys and projects has become harder to secure in recent years. It is therefore difficult to determine the precise status of the water vole across the UK at the current time. However, the national Water Vole Database and Mapping Project (the source of the recent data mentioned above), has identified the important areas for water voles across the country by collating available data since 2008.

Water vole on a mat of water crowfoot.

The UK Water Vole Steering Group set up the Water Vole Database and Mapping Project in 2008 in order 'to assess the national status and trend of the species and to report against national BAP targets'. Funded by the Environment Agency, Royal Society of Wildlife Trusts and the People's Trust for Endangered Species, the aim of the project is to centralise the storage and management of all data on water vole and mink and to continually update it. By using geographical information systems, data on water voles and their habitat can be mapped accurately and analysed in order to target conservation effort in key areas. These key areas are ranked according to numbers and densities of populations from 'local key areas' that have several robust colonies within six-kilometre squares to 'regional key areas' where there are populations of water voles throughout 30 five-kilometre squares that may 'persist for more than 40 years'. In other words, this is the hope for the future – a landscape-wide presence of water voles that could be the target for conservation efforts to conserve the species into the future. Derbyshire's upland populations of water voles are classified as being within regional key areas.

In addition to this project, the People's Trust for Endangered Species is working with partners to establish a national monitoring programme for the water vole. This programme will annually revisit the sites that were surveyed during the 1989–1990 and 1996–1998 Vincent Wildlife Trust water vole surveys and will supplement the National Water Vole Database and Mapping Project. It is to be hoped that, together, these projects will provide a more complete picture of the current status and distribution of the water vole across the UK.

In Derbyshire there is currently no funding at work specifically targeted for water voles. Derbyshire County Council faces massive budget cuts:

'In the countryside service we are losing over a third of our budget over the next few years. So something has to give somewhere. Our priorities and what we're focusing on is constantly changing. You've still got conservation in your heart and that's what we're all here for but we have to think more about the public access side of things now. With austerity hitting and with us not being a statutory body with statutory duties if the money gets tighter and tighter they will focus on the things they have to do so we could drop off the end of the scale.'
IAIAN STAFFORD

But Derbyshire Wildlife Trust suggests one of the best ways to overcome the lack of funding is to empower the public:

'We encourage people to look out for water voles and report their sightings to us. Imagine how precise national records and subsequent conservation work would be if everyone in the UK knew to do this.'
KAITE HELPS

The importance of reedbeds as refuges for water voles

It is now accepted that the total eradication of American mink cannot be achieved in Britain, so attention has been focused on large populations of water voles that have managed to prevail in the presence of mink. Typically, the areas where water vole and mink appear to coexist have extensive non-linear habitat in the form of reedbeds.

Reedbeds and marshes are inaccessible and so are very difficult to survey. They are also difficult to penetrate for predators and this may be the very thing that protects water voles in such habitats. The possibility that reedbeds could provide important refuge areas for water voles has important implications for the conservation of the species, and so research supported by the People's Trust for Endangered Species and English Nature was undertaken by Carter and Bright.[8] They 'investigated sources of overwinter (September 1999–April 2000) mortality of water voles and their behavioural perception of predation risk at reedbed sites where mink were present'.

Carter and Bright selected three sites in Kent, Suffolk and Somerset that all had large water vole populations and uncontrolled mink presence. The sites had varying combinations of wet grazing, wet woodland, ponds and reedbeds made up principally of common reed (*Phragmites australis*). All the sites had networks of channels of varying widths running through the reedbeds. Across the three sites, water voles were trapped and classified according to age and gender with only those weighing above 150 grams chosen for the study. Seventy water voles were fitted with radio transmitters that were heat sensitive and would pulse when a water vole had died. Nine lost their collars or went out of range and of those left in the trial (61), six more went missing 'presumed dead' and 33 were predated. The overall mortality at 64 per cent (principally through predation by mustelids – mainly considered to be mink) was not very far off the national average of 70 per cent of overwintering water voles. The difference lay in the varying locations of where the animals were killed.

TOP: Bearded tit in reedbed. BOTTOM: Female reed bunting.

8) Carter and Bright, 'Reedbeds as refuges for water voles (Arvicola terrestris) from predation by introduced mink (Mustela vison)' in *Biological Conservation*, Vol.111 (2003).

Carter and Bright found that the proportion of animals predated 'declined steeply with the distance from the main channel' and that those whose centre of activity was 150 metres from the main channel had half the risk of those living just ten metres from the main channel. The 'main channels' were classified as those over ten metres wide.

Water voles living in reedbeds make nests in the summer but go underground into communal burrows in the winter. Reedbeds with islands away from the main channel appeared to offer the best refuge. It may just be that mink find it harder to work through the dense, tricky territory and instead prey along the margins where there are richer and easier pickings to be had, such as moorhens, coots and ducks, or unwary water voles. The predation of overwintering water voles (that spend more time in burrows) would inevitably involve predominantly mustelids, as herons, owls and foxes cannot get to them. In spring and summer reedbed territory continues to be hard for most predators to negotiate.

By calculating average mortality rates at 30 per cent, Carter and Bright estimated that if water voles overwintered 150 metres away from the main channel and their rates of predation were only 30 per cent, with average summer increase in numbers by breeding (which also takes account of the high average rates of mortality) 'such water vole populations would more than double each year'. The implications of this for the future conservation of the species are clear – reedbeds are crucial and an expansion of this habitat is vital.

The other aspect of the research was measuring water voles' perception of predation risk at Stodmarsh, the largest of the three sites studied. Feeding stations close by latrines and burrow entrances were supplied with chopped carrots at distances of both one metre from bankside vegetation cover and at five metres from cover. Some of these were placed at the edge of the reedbed and close to the main channel (those over ten metres wide) and some were placed deep in the reedbed at least 50 metres away from any significant channel. They measured food left behind and came up with a measure of 'giving up' densities. They found that the water voles' sense of danger or threat (that would interrupt their feeding, thus 'giving up'), was much higher at the five-metre distance from cover than when they were close to cover at just one metre. However there was no difference at all in their perception of predator threat from deep within the reedbed, or close by the main channel where all the danger lies. This lack of perceived danger is there to be seen by anyone lucky enough to watch a water vole that will soon dive for the nearest cover if disturbed. Most have no deep cover to retreat to, so they make the best of what there is; but thousands of years of residence along the margins of watercourses has not prepared them for the American mink.

OPPOSITE PAGE: Female reed bunting

'Reedbeds, and perhaps other refuges, may support source populations that are likely to increase the viability of water vole metapopulations in surrounding landscapes through dispersal. Reedbeds and other refuges could thus be a focus from which to build the metapopulation management (Macdonald and Strachan, 1999; Lambin et al., 2001) that is probably essential for conserving water vole colonies that are now highly fragmented. Such a conservation programme has now begun in England and Wales. In practice, it will be important to ensure that there are sufficient steep-sided earth banks within reedbeds to provide sites for burrows above likely flood levels (Lawton and Woodroffe, 1991). Ideally, networks of steep-sided islands should be created within large reedbeds as overwintering refuges. These should be as far as possible from main water channels and their creation needs to be offset by the retention of areas of wet reedbed without islands, which may be important to water voles in the summer. Finally, we suggest that the use of natural refuges from predation in general could be much more frequently exploited by conservationists to combat the vast global impact of non-native predators.' Carter and Bright (2003).

Sadly for us, we may have to make do with knowing that water voles still exist high in the uplands along remote catchment streams or tucked away deep in reedbeds and marshes. The delight of watching them along our rivers, streams and canals may become an increasingly rare experience.

Climate change and extreme weather

The summer of 2011 was the fourth driest ever recorded and it followed on from a dry winter that was also the coldest on record with freezing temperatures that reached arctic conditions and continued for months. A local farmer told me that his tractor temperature gauge showed -25° Celsius on one of the coldest mornings. In 2011, all over Britain, crops failed, rivers dried up and people experienced severe water shortages. In December, torrential rain over many days recharged the rivers. Later, 2012 became the year of floods. Many towns and villages, farms and businesses were flooded repeatedly through the year as new rainfall records were broken.

Within a few months rivers across the country went from record low levels to the highest levels ever and floods became a regular feature of our local and national news for much of the year. We were experiencing what people across the globe have had to contend with for decades. Climate scientists are agreed that extreme and unpredictable weather is a consequence of the climate changing.

In the River Bradford the endangered white-clawed crayfish had to be rescued and many fish died in all of our rivers. Water voles, while being proficient swimmers, are not able to cope with strong, fast currents. They are known to carry their young to higher burrows when water levels rise, but if caught unawares by flash floods they are likely to drown. Fast-flowing rivers can aid in dispersal but the kind of catastrophic floods that we have witnessed across Britain can devastate water vole populations. A combination of drought and flood may partially account for the apparent collapse in water vole numbers between 2011 and 2013.

Water voles need watercourses to have a permanent depth of at least 25 centimetres, so drought causes them major problems when channels become too shallow or disappear altogether. Dry conditions also cause bank structures to disintegrate and when vegetation dies off they are left exposed and without food.

Forty years ago, drought had a major impact on Derbyshire's water voles as observed by the Sorby Natural History Society: 'In 1977 the number of recorded water voles decreased, following the severe droughts of 1975 and 1976, and several observers commented that the species appeared to be less common than in previous years … but by 1979, the number of records was more or less back to the pre 1976 level.' Derek Whiteley and Valerie Clinging, *Mammals of the Sheffield Area*.

OPPOSITE PAGE, TOP LEFT: The River Bradford dried out in October 2011. **Photo**: Andrew McCloy. TOP RIGHT: The River Bradford flooded by summer rain.
BOTTOM LEFT: A water vole rescues its baby from a flooded burrow on Press Brook. **Photo**: Jim Green. BOTTOM RIGHT: The River Derwent flooded in autumn.

It is doubtful that today's depleted populations of water voles could make such a rapid recovery. Drought has undoubtedly caused many local extinctions in Derbyshire where fluctuating levels in rivers have caused problems for wildlife. Watercourses have been modified and exploited by people throughout history for mills, fishing and mining, and we still live with the consequences of centuries of lead mining that altered the hydrology of much of the White Peak, causing low flows in many rivers. Water supply on the high limestone plateau has always been a problem and most of the farms in the area have licences to take or 'abstract' groundwater from boreholes. This practice has been contentious in times of drought when groundwater levels have become very low, with rivers and streams badly affected. Throughout Britain, the Environment Agency has sought to limit abstraction licences as the precious resource of water is monitored and conserved with greater care than ever before.

In the 21st century we face the challenges of extreme weather caused by climate change, with both drought and flood having massive impacts in town and countryside. In this context, very often the needs of wild creatures are seen by many to be at odds with the needs of people. But now, increasingly, there is a greater understanding that a disrupted environment damages us all and that there is an artificial choice between the needs of the natural world and the perceived needs of humans. Building on the floodplain has caused flooding and damaged homes and businesses as well as disrupting the natural environment. Dumping chemicals into our rivers puts people as well as wild creatures at risk. We are destroying insects and losing pollinators that ultimately make it possible to grow our food. Sensitive management of moorlands, woods and grasslands does not just benefit wildlife, because these landscapes function as carbon sinks, and they are also our best flood defences.

Uplands, moors and grasslands are nature's sponges, collecting and storing rainfall and helping to regulate the flow of our rivers. Careful management of landscapes and watercourses is key to how we adapt to the challenges of the future. Caring for our ecosystems and the creatures that depend on them is ultimately about self-preservation. The very landscapes which may be the last refuges for the water vole – our wetlands and moors – need protection and sensitive management for all of our sakes.

View west to Kinder Scout from Bleaklow – bleak upland territory in which water voles can be found living in the headstreams.

What water voles can do

Water voles can do a great job themselves. They are
a robust species capable of making fast recoveries.
One female can produce as many as 30 offspring in one
year. They have the capacity to flourish – they are rodents
after all – low down the food chain and with an inbuilt
mechanism that means that in optimal conditions their
breeding capacity could compensate for high mortality.
But populations need to be bigger in order to persist.

If just 30 per cent of a population survives the winter
to breed in the spring then 30 voles from a hundred is
a better start than just three surviving from a population
of ten. Small populations die out. Water voles are
immensely productive in their short lives and they
know exactly how and where they want to live. If we
can just take some of the pressure off them, they could
expand and become part of our landscape once more,
to charm and delight future generations.

What we can do

Water vole pup.

Enormous amounts of detailed research has been carried out by scientists since the groundbreaking work of the 1990s, and armies of ecologists, naturalists and enthusiastic volunteers are all trying to work out how best to secure the future of the water vole. If a tide of goodwill and expertise were enough to save the water vole it would now be flourishing, but the environmental impacts of non-native problem species, climate change, agricultural intensification and ever-increasing pressure of leisure pursuits in our crowded island have made the habitable world of the water vole ever smaller and more threatened. But we can all contribute in some way to securing a future for the water vole so that future generations can watch this enchanting animal, that somehow epitomises the gentle, intimate and quiet life lived by wild creatures along our rivers, streams, canals and lakes.

This book offers a challenge and an entreaty: we can all do something to help the water vole and other threatened aquatic species. We can do something big by becoming a volunteer for the Wildlife Trusts, or report what we see to them, or we can just learn to behave better and to consider the small lives lived along our waterways – learn to be quiet, to keep the dog on the lead and out of the water. We can learn to be invisible, to listen and watch, and by doing so gain some of the greatest rewards it is possible to have in our rushed and crowded lives – to see a wild animal living its life in peace.

Baby water voles in spring.

appendices

APPENDIX 1

Landscape Character Areas

Every area of Britain has habitats and ecosystems that have evolved from the unique interactions between the natural environment and the uses that man has made of it. The conservation movement has recognised the need to assess priorities for action within landscape-wide targets based on the unique characteristics of broad tracts of land.

In recognition of this, the Countryside Commission (now Natural England) identified 120 'Natural Areas' in England defined as 'biogeographic zones which reflect the geological foundation, the natural systems and processes and the wildlife in different parts of England, and provide a framework for setting objectives for nature conservation' (*Biodiversity: The UK Steering Group Report*, HMSO, 1995). A later development of this framework led to the creation of a 'Character Map of England' identifying 159 'Joint Character Areas'. In 2005 this map was updated and Natural England supported by English Heritage produced the 'Character of England Landscape, Wildlife and Cultural Features Map', which maintained 159 of what became known as National Character Areas.

Within Derbyshire there are eight National Character Areas (NCAs). In the Peak District National Park there are three – the Dark Peak, the White Peak and the South-West Peak. These areas extend beyond Derbyshire into Cheshire, Staffordshire and Yorkshire. In the rest of Derbyshire, which will be referred to as Lowland Derbyshire, there are seven National Character Areas: Derbyshire Peak Fringe and Lower Derwent; the Nottinghamshire, Derbyshire and Yorkshire Coalfield; Southern Magnesian Limestone; Needwood and South Derbyshire Claylands; Trent Valley Washlands; Leicestershire and South Derbyshire Coalfield; and Melbourne Parklands. Most of these areas cross county and other administrative boundaries, and conservation efforts within them usually involve a number of partnerships with different agencies and public authorities involved.

What follows is an outline of the broad landscape areas within the two parts of Derbyshire, the Peak District National Park and Lowland Derbyshire, and the geology that shaped them.

Geology

The foundations of Derbyshire's landscapes and river systems were formed by geological and climatic events in the early part of what is called the Carboniferous period. The limestone of the White Peak is made from the remains of sea creatures that formed layers of sediment on the floor of a shallow tropical sea between 310 and 360 million years ago. The younger rocks of the Dark Peak (the millstone grit) were made from sediments that washed down through a gigantic river delta from mountains that were eroding far to the north.

Over millions of years, extreme pressure compressed and hardened the gravel, sand and mud of the delta into layers of gritstones, sandstones and shales that lay over the limestone. The mud and other fine materials settled out to form shales, and coarser materials produced the millstone grit of the Dark Peak. The swampy delta was forested and it was the compression and eventual fossilisation of the remains of the delta's trees and other plants that formed the coal measures, which now lie either side of the Peak District.

Seismic forces (over millions of years) raised the Derbyshire Dome – a rise of land known as an anticline on an axis running from north to south. The high (3,000-metre) 'dome' was worn down over time to reveal the limestone of the White Peak, the oldest rock of the Peak District. High ground composed of the millstone grit of the Dark Peak has formed a horseshoe shape to the north, east and west of the Derbyshire Dome.

Ice and water

The impact of glacial action on the north of the county is evident in the steep-sided gorges through the Carboniferous limestone that were scoured out by great volumes of meltwater from thawing snowfields. As these volumes of water no longer flow, there are many dry valleys in the White Peak and rivers that flow underground in drier seasons.

The Late Devensian ice sheets did not extend beyond the outer edges of the Dark Peak to reach Derbyshire but did cover much of Wales and Cheshire extending to the south-west of Staffordshire. The wide, flat valley floors of the Dove and the Trent reflect the flow of glacial meltwater from the west.

The Peak District National Park

The Dark and the White Peak centres on these two distinct zones with their different geology and vegetation adjacent to one other. The Dark Peak, with its high, acidic mountain plateau covered with blanket bog and heather moorlands, and the White Peak, with its rolling pastures and deep limestone gorges, made these areas an obvious choice to become Britain's first national park in 1951.

The large urban centres of Manchester, Sheffield and Stoke-on-Trent, and the smaller towns of Macclesfield, Chesterfield and Buxton, bound the Peak District National Park on all sides. The national park reaches into Staffordshire, Cheshire and South Yorkshire but it occupies well over 40 per cent of the land space of Derbyshire.

Lowland Derbyshire

THE COAL MEASURES

The Derbyshire coal measures are in the east of the county between Eckington and Ilkeston, bordering on Nottinghamshire with another outcrop at Swadlincote south of Derby. At the time of nationalisation in 1947, 60,000 people were employed in 68 collieries in Derbyshire. The last to close in 1993 were the Markham and Shirebrook collieries.

The associated industries of iron and brick making had also flourished in this eastern part of the county and while the industries have gone, these remain the most populace parts of the county. While Derbyshire's coal mines are gone, restoration of some former sites has created important wildlife habitats.

MAGNESIAN LIMESTONE

The narrow band of rare magnesian limestone forms a low plateau east of the coal measures. Bolsover Castle and Hardwick Hall are prominent landmarks on the west-facing edge of the plateau.

This is productive agricultural land which is cut through by shallow valleys, cave systems and rocky gorges. The most famous gorge is Creswell Crags which is a Site of Special Scientific Interest (SSSI) and a World Heritage Site with globally important traces of early man as well as bird, fish and mammal bone assemblages.

THE PEAK FRINGE

The Peak Fringe is the NCA that lies in the heart of and wholly within Derbyshire, bordered by the Dark and White Peak to the west and the coal measures to the east. The Derwent valley runs through the centre of the Peak Fringe with the Derwent Valley Mills World Heritage Site located where the River Derwent once supplied power to the 18th-century mills that were the world's first factories. The valley floor is wide in some places with extensive areas of floodplain grassland.

THE SOUTH DERBYSHIRE CLAYLANDS

This area stretches from the western county boundary formed by the River Dove to Derby in the east. Most of the area is characterised by a low-lying pastoral landscape with gentle rolling hills with underlying sandstones and marls (limey clays). Ashbourne to the north is the largest settlement in this predominantly quiet rural corner of Derbyshire, but there has been considerable urban expansion of Derby and Burton and increased housing development in the villages.

THE TRENT VALLEY AND NATIONAL FOREST

The mainly flat or slightly undulating landscape of the south of Derbyshire is dominated by the floodplains of the Trent and Dove. Meltwater from the ice sheets of the last (Devensian) glaciation washed south and eastwards to deposit the sands and gravels of the lower Dove and Trent valleys.

The gravel terraces of the Trent have been exploited for decades. Extraction of these valuable minerals involved pumping out water leaving gravel pits, many of which were later filled and returned to agricultural use. However many of the old extraction sites have formed a chain of wetland reserves managed by Derbyshire Wildlife Trust including at Hilton situated in the floodplain of the Dove, also Drakelow and Willington Gravel Pits.

THE NATIONAL FOREST

The National Forest area includes the Melbourne Parklands, lying between the Trent and the southern Derbyshire coalfield around Swadlincote. This area includes Carboniferous limestone, millstone grit and sandstones. The landscape here is characterised by undulating mixed farmland and large estates with extensive parkland and ancient woodland including the historic Calke Abbey now owned by the National Trust. Staunton Harold (adjoining the Calke Abbey estate) and Foremark reservoirs are the largest areas of open water which were formerly occupied by water voles.

The southern Derbyshire coalfield is centred around Swadlincote. Now the coal mines, brickworks, pipeyards and potteries associated with the coalfield are long gone and the last colliery, Cadley Hill, closed in 1988. The legacy of these industries together with opencast mining had left vast tracts of derelict land that has now become the centre of the National Forest. As well as planting of broad-leaved and coniferous woodland in the 1990s, areas of open grassland and many ponds have been created which may provide suitable habitat for recovering water vole populations in the future.

APPENDIX 2

The national water vole and mink surveys: 1989–1990 and 1996–1998

The two national water vole and mink surveys were conducted by the Vincent Wildlife Trust in the first systematic collection of data on these species. The whole of Britain was divided along the lines of the National Grid, and sites on representative watercourses chosen that were evenly distributed across England, Scotland and Wales. A grid of the same 18 x 10-kilometre squares in each 100 kilometres of the National Grid was chosen and within each of the chosen 10-kilometre squares, five sites were selected for survey. Every 100-kilometre square of mainland Britain had 90 survey sites making a total of 1,926. An additional 1,044 sites were drawn from old published records, local and county mammal reports, county museum records and various local and national survey data that provided evidence of water vole occupation from 1900 to 1989. Historical sites were chosen at a distance from those more randomly chosen sites to allow for greater overall coverage. The eventual number of survey sites was 2,970, each of which were visited over 24 months from 1989 to 1990. These sites were established in the first survey referred to as the 'baseline survey', to measure the range and populations of both water vole and mink in order to assess changes in a follow-up survey seven years later (1996 to 1998).

The 600-metre-long linear sites extending along waterways were examined 300 metres upstream from a midway point, then 300 metres downstream for signs of both water vole and mink occupation. The presence of water voles was established by recording field signs, with positive presence recorded only by droppings, latrines or animals seen. The presence of mink was recorded if mink scats, footprints, or dead or live mink were detected.

APPENDIX 3

Useful organisations

Derbyshire Wildlife Trust:
www.derbyshirewildlifetrust.org.uk

Derbyshire Mammal Group:
www.derbyshiremammalgroup.com

Sorby Natural History Society:
www.sorby.org.uk

Peak District National Park Authority:
www.peakdistrict.gov.uk

The Wildlife Trusts:
www.wildlifetrusts.org

The Mammal Society:
www.mammal.org.uk

National Trust:
www.nationaltrust.org.uk

Vincent Wildlife Trust:
www.vwt.org.uk

Natural England:
www.gov.uk/government/
organisations/natural-england

**People's Trust for Endangered
Species:** ptes.org

**Game & Wildlife Conservation
Trust:** www.gwct.org.uk

**Department for Environment,
Food and Rural Affairs (Defra):**
www.gov.uk/government/
organisations/department-for-
environment-food-rural-affairs

Environment Agency:
www.gov.uk/government/
organisations/environment-agency

Kingfisher.

Bibliography

Ashton, N.M., Lewis, S.G. and Stringer, C.B., eds., *The Ancient Human Occupation of Britain (Developments in Quarternary Science)* (Amsterdam: Elsevier, 2010).

Barkham, P., 'British water vole population slumps by more than one-fifth, survey finds', *The Guardian* [online] (6 September 2013). <http://www.theguardian.com/environment/2013/sep/06/water-vole-population-slump>

Bates, K., *The status of water voles (Arvicola terrestris) on the upper reaches of the river Dove* (Unpublished undergraduate thesis, Nottingham: Nottingham Trent University, 2004).

Bonesi, L. and Macdonald, D.W., 'Impact of released Eurasian otters on a population of American mink: a test using an experimental approach', *OIKOS*, Vol.106, No.1 (July 2004), pp9–18.

Carrington, D., 'Earth has lost half of its wildlife in the past 40 years, says WWF', *The Guardian* [online] (30 September 2014). <http://www.theguardian.com/environment/2014/sep/29/earth-lost-50-wildlife-in-40-years-wwf>

Carter, S.P. and Bright, P.W., 'Reedbeds as refuges for water voles (Arvicola terrestris) from predation by introduced mink (Mustela vison)', *Biological Conservation*, Vol.111, (2003), pp371–376.

Ceballos, G., Ehrlich, P.R., Barnosky, A.D., García, A., Pringle., R.M. and Palmer, T.M., 'Accelerated modern human-induced species losses: Entering the sixth mass extinction', *Science Advances*, Vol.1, No.5 (19 June 2015).

Clay, P., *An Archaeological Resource Assessment and Research Agenda for The Neolithic and Early-Middle Bronze Age of the East Midlands* (Leicester: University of Leicester, 2001).

Clinging, V. and Whiteley, D., *Mammals of the Sheffield Area*, (Sheffield: Sorby Natural History Society and Sheffield City Museums, 1980).

Collis, J., *Wigber Low, Derbyshire: A Bronze Age and Anglian Burial Site in the White Peak* (Sheffield: Department of Prehistory and Archaeology, University of Sheffield, 1983).

Department for Environment, Food and Rural Affairs (Defra), *Biodiversity 2020: A strategy for England's wildlife and ecosystem services* [online] (London, 2011). <https://www.gov.uk/government/publications/biodiversity-2020-a-strategy-for-england-s-wildlife-and-ecosystem-services>

— *The Natural Choice: securing the value of nature* [online] (London, 2011). <https://www.gov.uk/government/publications/the-natural-choice-securing-the-value-of-nature>

— *Farming statistics: livestock populations at 1 December 2013* [online] (London, 2014). <https://www.gov.uk/government/statistics/farming-statistics-livestock-populations-at-1-december-2013-uk>

Derbyshire Wildlife Trust and National Trust, *Water Voles in the Uplands* (Belper, 2004).

Derbyshire Wildlife Trust, *Internal report for sites surveyed by staff* (Unpublished, 2014).

— *Water Vole Monitoring Handbook* (2008).

— *Otter Monitoring Handbook* (2008).

— *Water for Wildlife* newsletter (2014).

— *Water for Wildlife* newsletter (2015).

Ecclesbourne Restoration Partnership, *An improvement plan for the River Ecclesbourne and its valley* (2013).

Environment Agency, *Water for life and livelihoods: River Basin Management Plan Humber River Basin District* (2009).

— 'Water voles return to every county in England', (press release) on *Gov.uk* [online] (2015). <https://www.gov.uk/government/news/water-voles-return-to-every-county-in-england>

Frost, R. and Shaw, S., eds., *The Birds of Derbyshire* (Liverpool: Liverpool University Press, 2013).

Game and Wildlife Conservation Trust (GWCT), *Mink in Britain* [online] (2014). <http://www.gwct.org.uk/wildlife/research/mammals/american-mink/mink-in-britain/>

Glover, S., *The History, Gazetteer, and Directory of the County of Derby* (Derby: Henry Mozley and Son, 1829).

Gow, D., 'Water vole reintroduction projects – the lessons and the success factors', *ECOS*, Vol.28 [online] (2007). <http://www.watervoles.com/index_htm_files/Water%20vole%20reintroduction%20projects.pdf>

Gow, D., Andrews, R. and Smith, D.W., 'Water vole mitigation guidance – Important updates for evidence-based good practice' on *Derek Gow Consultancy Ltd* [online] (2012). <http://www.watervoles.com/index_htm_files/water%20vole%20mitigation%20guidance.pdf>

Greenpeace UK, 'The Poison Factory: The story of Coalite Chemicals' on *The Skeptic Tank* [online] (1993). <http://www.skeptictank.org/treasure/GP4/POISON.TXT>

Gregory, C.L., *A River in Time* (Bakewell: Grafika, 2013).

Harris, S. and Yalden, D.W., eds., *Mammals of the British Isles (4th edn)* (Southampton: Mammal Society, 2008).

HM Government, 'Wildlife and Countryside Act 1981 (as amended)' on *Legislation.gov.uk* [online] (1981). <http://www.legislation.gov.uk/ukpga/1981/69>

Hochstein, J.R., Aulerich, R.J. and Bursian, S.J., 'Acute Toxicity of 2,3,7,8-tetrachlorodibenzo-p-dioxin to mink' in *Arch. Environ. Contam. Toxicol.*, Vol.17, No.1 (1988), pp33–37.

Jefferies, D.J., ed., *The water vole and mink survey of Britain 1996–1998 with a history of long-term changes in the status of both species and their causes* (Ledbury: Vincent Wildlife Trust, 2003).

Joint Nature Conservation Committee (JNNC), 'UK Priority Species data collation: Arvicola terrestris version 2 updated on 15/12/2010' on *Joint Nature Conservation Committee* [online]. <http://jncc.defra.gov.uk/_speciespages/115.pdf>

Jones, M.E., *The End of Roman Britain* (Ithaca: Cornell University Press, 1996).

Jourdain, F.C.R., 'Mammals', in Page, W. ed., *The Victoria History of the County of Derby*, Vol.1 (London: Constable, 1905), pp150–159.

Lovegrove, R., *Silent Fields: the long decline of a nation's wildlife* (Oxford: Oxford University Press, 2007).

Lowland Derbyshire Biodiversity Partnership, *Lowland Derbyshire Biodiversity Action Plan* [online] (2011). <http://www.derbyshirebio-diversity.org.uk/lbaps/lowland-derbyshire.php>

Lowland Derbyshire Biodiversity Partnership, 'Water Vole Species Action Plan 2005–2010' in *Lowland Derbyshire Local Biodiversity Action Plan* [online] (2006). <http://www.derbyshirebiodiversity.org.uk/lbaps/sap/Water_Vole_SAP.pdf>

Mallon, D., Alston, D. and Whiteley. D., *The Mammals of Derbyshire* (Derbyshire Mammal Group and Sorby Natural History Society, 2012).

Mathieson, K., 'England's water voles in desperate decline', *The Guardian* [online] (11 May 2015). <http://www.theguardian.com/environment/2015/may/11/englands-water-voles-in-desperate-decline>

McGuire, C., Whitfield, D. and Perkins, H., *National Water Vole Database and Mapping Project: Guide to the Use of Project Outputs to End of 2011* (2013).

Middleton, J.F., *Mammals of the Derby Area* (Derby: Derby Junior Naturalists, 1969).

Millett, M., *The Romanization of Britain* (Cambridge: Cambridge University Press, 1990).

Morris, P.A., Morris, M.J., MacPherson, D., Jefferies, D.J., Strachan, R. and Woodroffe, G.L., 'Estimating numbers of the water vole Arvicola terrestris: a correction to the published method', *Journal of Zoology*, Vol.246, (1998), pp61–62.

National Biodiversity Network (NBN) Gateway, Arvicola amphibious national species datasets, (2015).

Natural England and Department for Environment, Food and Rural Affairs (Defra), 'Water voles: surveys and mitigation for development projects' on *Gov.uk* [online] (2014). <https://www.gov.uk/water-voles-protection-surveys-and-licences>

Natural England, 'Water voles – the law in practice: guidance for planners and developers' [online] (2008). <http://webarchive.nationalarchives.gov.uk/20140605090108/http://naturalengland.org.uk/ourwork/regulation/wildlife/species/watervoles.aspx>

— 'Corporate Report: National Character Area profiles' on *Gov.uk* [online] (2014). See NCAs: 23, 24, 25, 29, 30, 31, 33, 40, 50, 51, 52, 68, 69, 70 and 71. <https://www.gov.uk/government/publications/national-character-area-profiles-data-for-local-decision-making/national-character-area-profiles>

— *Derbyshire Dales National Nature Reserve* [leaflet] (2014).

— *Otter: European protected species (Species Information Note SIN006)* [leaflet] (2007).

Peak District National Park Authority (PDNPA), *A Living Landscape: A Biodiversity Action Plan for the Peak District* (Bakewell, 2000).

— *Peak District State of the Park Report* [online] (2013). <http://www.peakdistrict.gov.uk/microsites/sopr/landscape/river-quality>

Perkins, H.M. and Mallon, D.P., *The Water Vole in Derbyshire* (Derby: Derbyshire Wildlife Trust, 1999).

Perkins, H.M., *Managing Land for Water Voles* (Derby: Derbyshire Wildlife Trust, 2005).

Piertney, S.B., Stewart. W.A., Lambin, X., Telfer, S., Aars, J. and Dallas, J.F., 'Phylogeographic structure and postglacial evolutionary history of water voles (Arvicola terrestris) in the United Kingdom', *Molecular Ecology*, Vol.14, (2005), pp1,435–1,444.

Reynolds, R., *The GWCT Mink Raft*, (Fordingbridge: Game and Wildlife Conservation Trust, 2003), rev. Short, M., Porteus, T., Rodgers, B. and Swan, M., (2013).

Ryder, S.R., *Water Voles (Animals of Britain no.4)* (London: Sunday Times, 1962), p12.

Schoon, N., 'Pollution watchdog plans legal action: Record levels of dioxins in river near Coalite plant', *The Independent* [online] (April 1994). <http://www.independent.co.uk/news/uk/pollution-watchdog-plans-legal-action-record-level-of-dioxins-in-river-near-coalite-plant-1372618.html>

Strachan, R., Moorhouse, T. and Gelling, M., *Water Vole Conservation Handbook (Third Edition)* (Oxford: WildCRU, 2011).

Strachan, R., *Water Voles (British Natural History Series)* (London: Whittet Books, 1997).

Telfer, S., Dallas, J.F., Aars, J., Piertney, S.B., Stewart, W.A. and Lambin, X., 'Demographic and genetic structure of fossorial water voles (Arvicola terrestris) on Scottish islands', *Journal of Zoology*, Vol.259, (2003), pp23–29.

Telfer, S., Holt, A., Donaldson, R. and Lambin, X., 'Metapopulation processes and persistence in remnant water vole populations', *OIKOS*, Vol.95, (2001), pp31–42.

Telfer, S., Piertney, S.B., Dallas, J.F., Stewart, W.A., Marshall, F., Gow, J.L. and Lambin, X., 'Parentage assignment detects frequent and large-scale dispersal in water voles', *Molecular Ecology*, Vol.12, (2003), pp1,939–1,949.

Walton, I. and Cotton, C., *The Compleat Angler; Or, The Contemplative Man's Recreation*, (5th edn, 1676).

Whiteley, D., ed., *The Natural History of the Sheffield Area and the Peak District* (Sheffield: Sorby Natural History Society, 1985.)

Woodroffe, G.L., *The Otter* (Southampton: The Mammal Society, 2007).

— *The Water Vole* (Southampton: The Mammal Society, 2000).

Woodroffe, G.L., Lawton, J.H. and Davidson, W.L., 'Patterns in the production of latrines by water voles (Arvicola terrestris) and their use as indices of abundance in population surveys', *Journal of Zoology*, Vol.220, (1990), pp439–445.

Yalden, D.W., *The History of British Mammals* (London: Poyser Natural History, 1999).

Zalasiewicz, J., 'The Earth stands on the brink of its sixth mass extinction and the fault is ours', *The Observer* [online] (21 June 2015). <http://www.theguardian.com/environment/2015/jun/21/mass-extinction-science-warning>

Zwiernik, M.J., Kay, D.P., Moore, J., Beckett, K.J, Khim, J.S., Newstead, J.L. Roark, S.A. and Giesy, J.P., 'Exposure and effects assessment of resident mink (Mustela vison) exposed to polychlorinated dibenzofurans and other dioxin-like compounds in the Tittabawassee River basin, Midland, Michigan, USA', *Environmental Toxicology and Chemistry*, Vol.27, No.10 (2008), pp2,076–2,087.

Acknowledgements

I have many people to thank for their time and expertise in the making of this book.

Thanks to Patricia Stubbs, Annie Neligan and Isabella Stone for their friendship, support and help in careful reading of various drafts at different stages and for their suggestions and comments. I am grateful to Kay Thompson who worked on Derbyshire Wildlife Trust's Water for Wildlife project, for her moral support, encouragement and advice, invaluable data input and close scrutiny of the text.

I wish to thank Debbie Alston, Mammal Recorder for Derbyshire, for her feedback, guidance and vital work with husband Dave Alston in producing the wonderful Derbyshire data maps. Also thanks to Helen Perkins, living landscape manager for the Wildlife Trusts, who supported this project from the beginning and has given generously of her time and specialist knowledge in reading the text, amending some errors and supplying all of the current national data maps from the National Water Vole Data and Mapping Project.

Thanks to Chris Wood, formerly project officer for the Water for Wildlife project at Derbyshire Wildlife Trust, for his excellent water vole survey training and setting me off on this venture in 2012. My thanks also to Elizabeth Woodward, Kieron Huston, Jane Proctor and Kaite Helps at Derbyshire Wildlife Trust for their support, documents and data.

Thanks to the staff at the Derbyshire Records Office and Local Studies Library for their friendly assistance. I have had some memorable days out with Colin Jones, secretary of the Peak Forest Angling Club, Warren Slaney, head river keeper for the Haddon Estate, Iaian Stafford, county council ranger for north-east Derbyshire, Bill Gordon, Peak District National Park ranger for the North Lees Estate, Con Meaney from the Old Waltonians fly fishing club, John Thomas for a memorable day in the wilder reaches of the Alport valley, Hilary Tann, whose beautiful photograph is featured on page 31, and several other people who have generously shown me round their patch of Derbyshire. I have learned much from these dedicated conservationists and enthusiasts and I thank them for their time and for sharing their special places and their thoughts with me.

Thanks are also due to Johnny Birks, ecological consultant and mammalogist, and Derek Gow, ecological consultant and specialist in water vole conservation, both of whom have guided me through some tricky mink and water vole territory with their great fund of knowledge, expertise and experience.

Thanks to Kirsty Lee who was most helpful in steering otters my way at the Chestnut Centre after 30 years of my trying (and failing) to photograph them in the wild.

Thanks to all the contributors to this book whose dedicated work and enthusiasm shines through in their words: Shirley Freeman, that great champion of Derbyshire's water voles and volunteer for the Derbyshire Wildlife Trust, Alan Heeley, ranger for north-east Derbyshire, and water vole guardians Janet and Jim Green, and Lu and Barbara Nolan.

I have Jon Barton at Vertebrate to thank for his support, commitment and backing of this project from the outset. Also John Coefield for weaving his way through the manuscript and steering this project to completion with great patience and attention to detail. Nathan Ryder for his fantastic design work and patience in sifting through over 2,000 images and bringing this water vole story to life. My thanks also to Tori Halliday and Teija Douglas at Vertebrate for their support, and to Susie Ryder for proofreading.

There are two people that I wish I was able to thank for their magnificent work for the water vole and many other species in Britain, and whose work is central to many of the ideas expressed in this book. While researching and writing I have thought often of the late Derek Yalden, former president of the Mammal Society, who I was privileged to know, and also the late Rob Strachan whose work on the water vole and the otter has been the foundation of conservation efforts for these species. The loss of these great scientists and field workers to wildlife conservation in Britain is as great as their contribution over many years of dedicated and groundbreaking work.

Finally, I must thank my partner Tony Mead who has lived with this book for 18 months, been the first to read each part of the text with meticulous care, has made numerous and always helpful suggestions, been stalwart in his support and whose fine mind and constructive criticism as well as encouragement and moral support have been indispensable to me – this book is dedicated to him.

While I have endeavoured to get things right, any errors are mine alone.

This adult water vole in early spring seemed to gaze straight at me for several minutes, but with its limited sight it was probably focused on the sound of the camera shutter clicking.